Easy to Moderate Mazes for Neuro Recovery

an exercise in attention and concentration

- phase I

Whether you or a loved one is recovering from a stroke, a head injury, or is experiencing problems with memory, brain exercises have been recommended as a supplement to cognitive-communication therapy.

As a speech-language pathologist, we always encourage brain exercises in combination with therapy to increase the opportunities for brain stimulation activities.

Mazes offer the benefits of first and foremost exercise among attention and concentration skills. They also target spatial learning and working memory.

The best part? Mazes are fun! You don't even feel like you are exercising your brain!

This is the first in a new series currently under development. Keep an eye out for more brain stimulation exercises coming your way soon!

Brain Power!

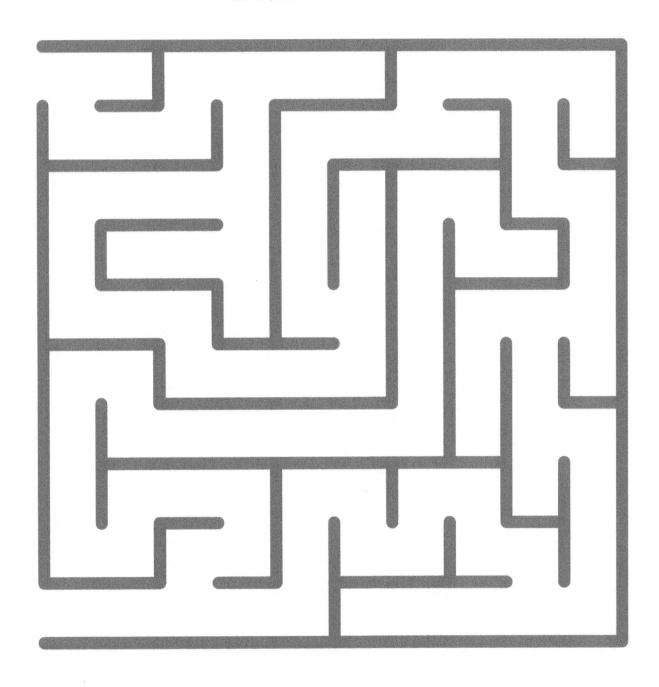

Brain Power!

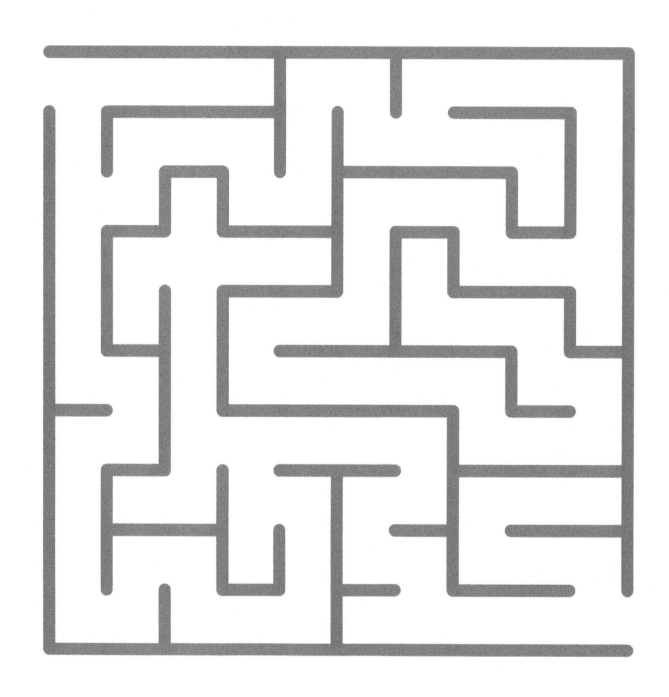

Brain Power!

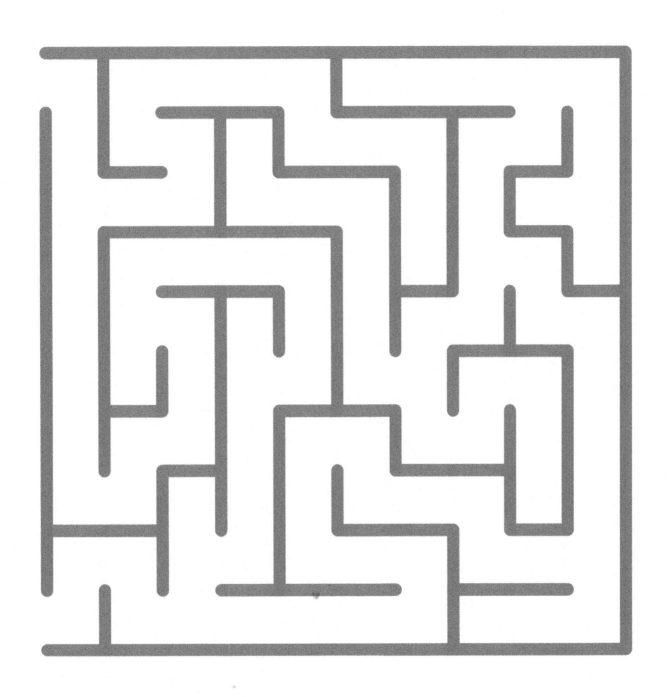

Brain Power!

Brain Power!

Brain Power!

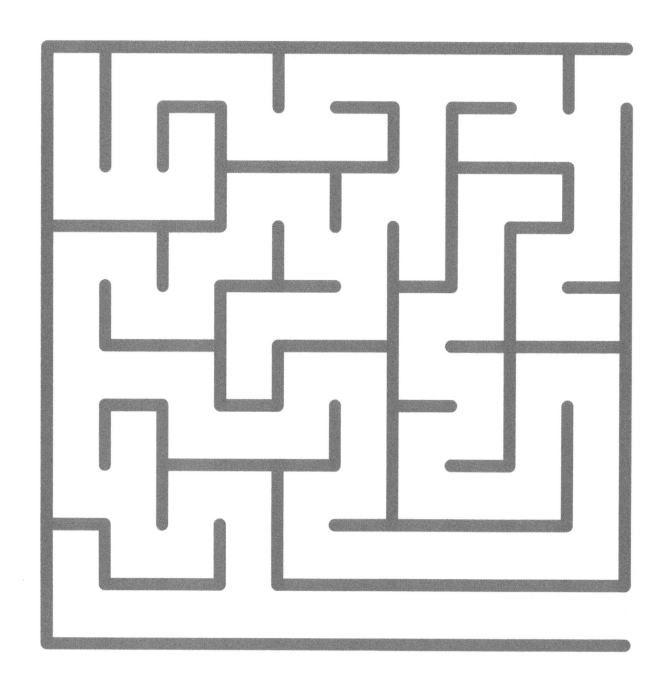

Brain Power!

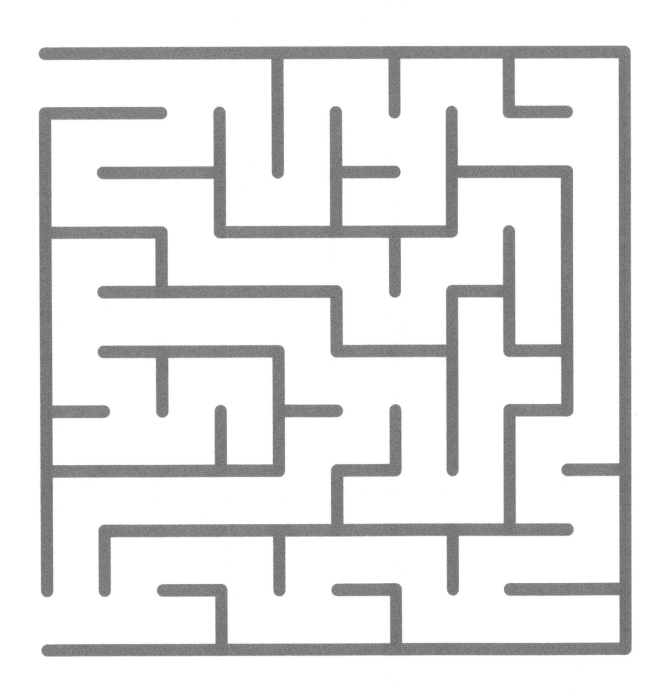

Brain Power!

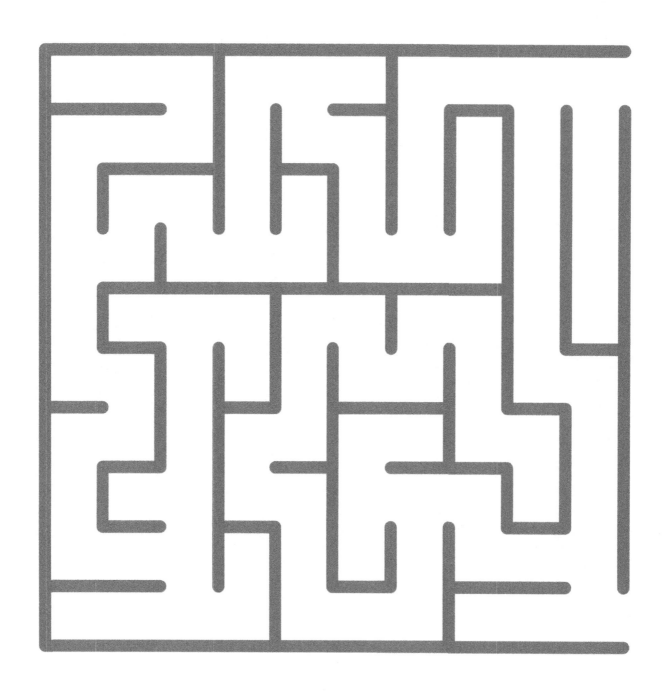

Brain Power!

Brain Power!

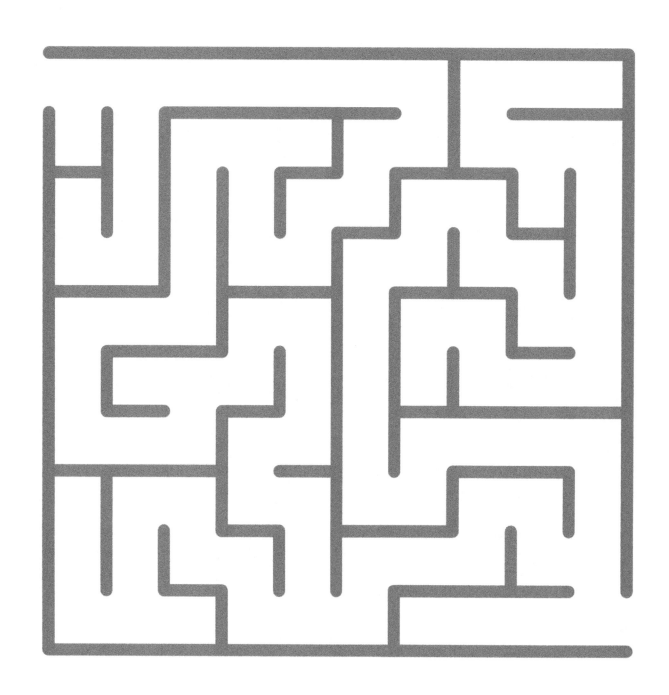

Brain Power!

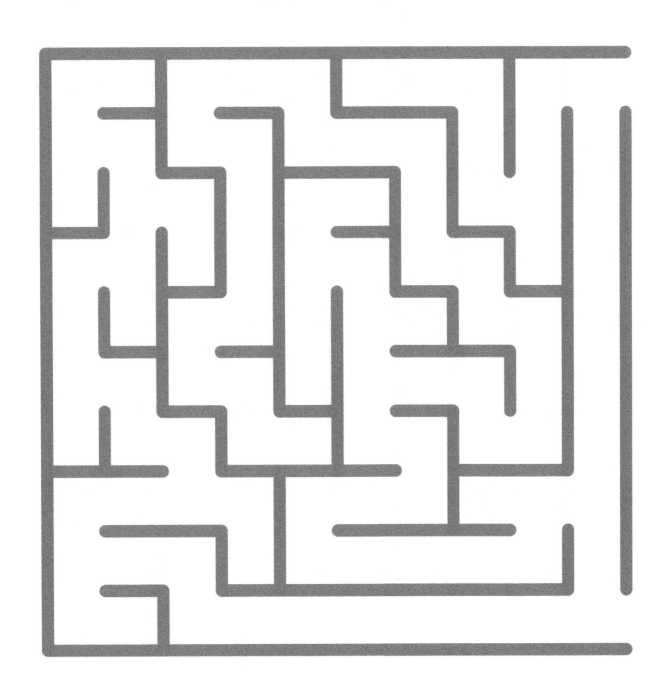

Brain Power!

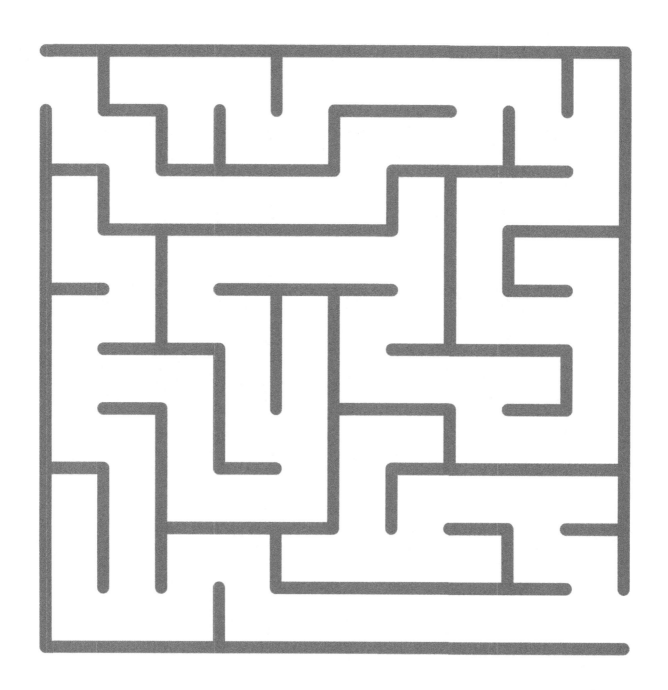

Brain Power!

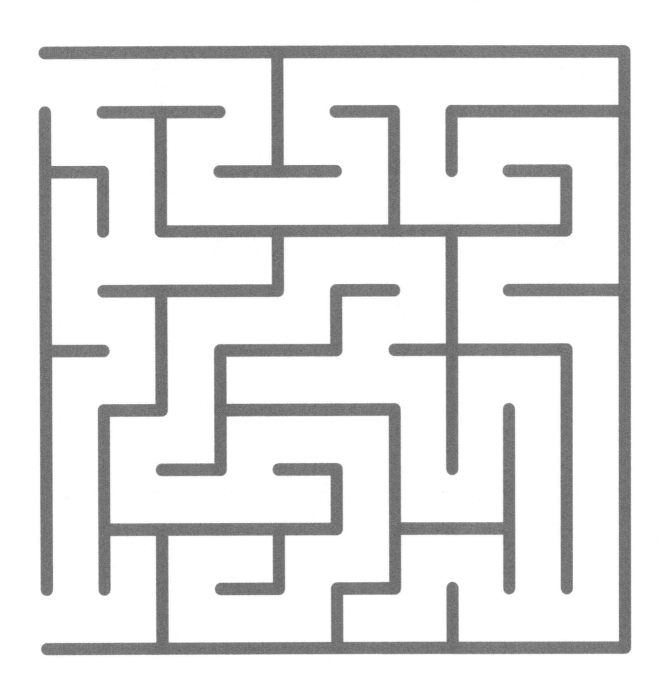

Brain Power!

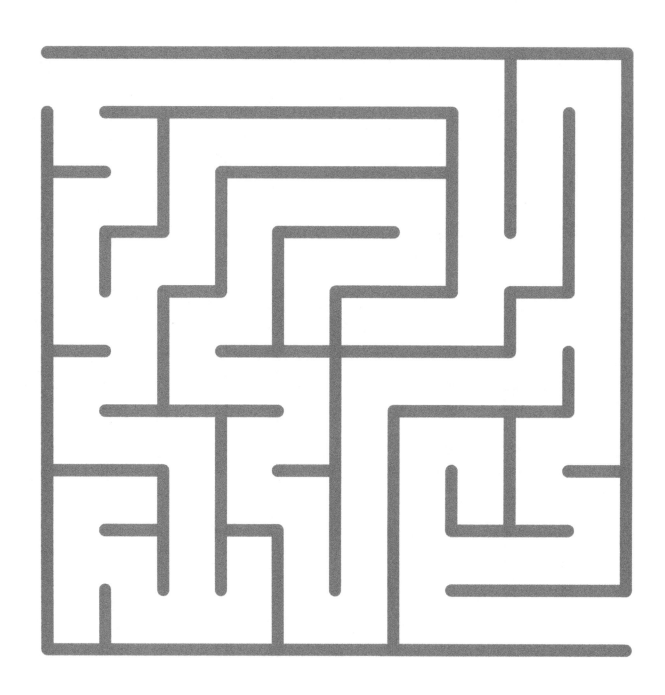

Brain Power!

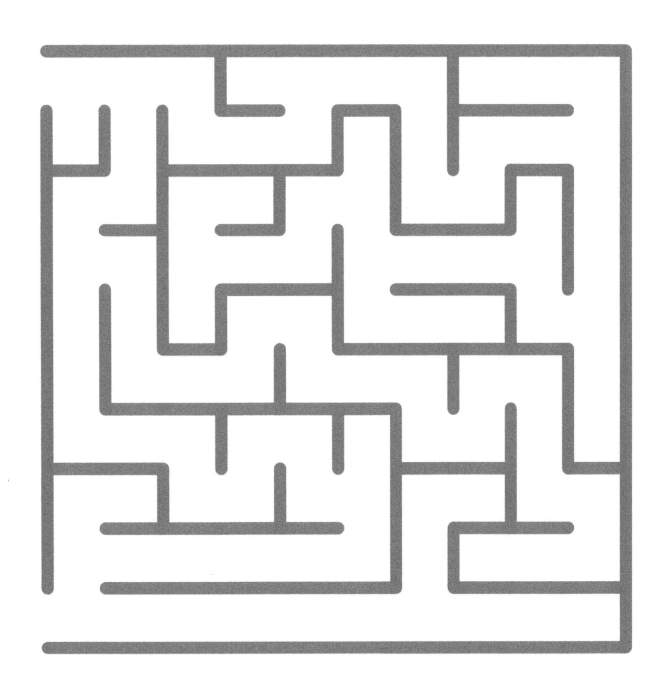

Brain Power!

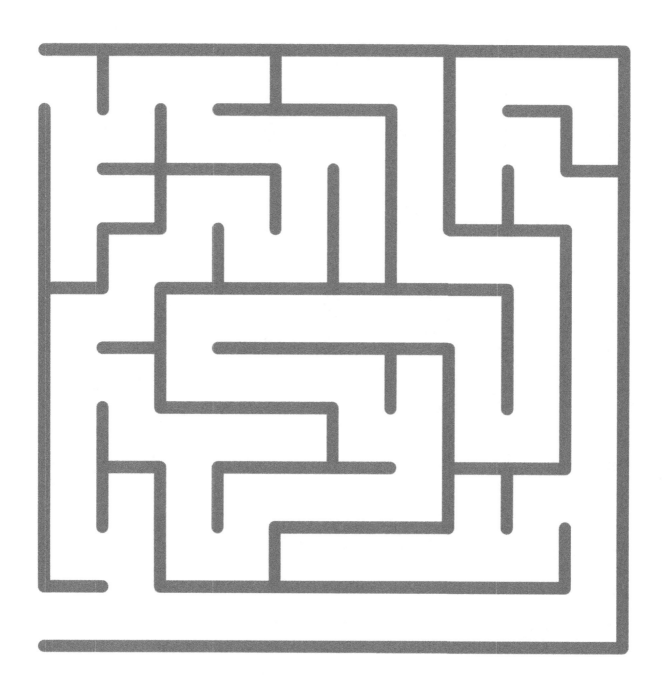

Brain Power!

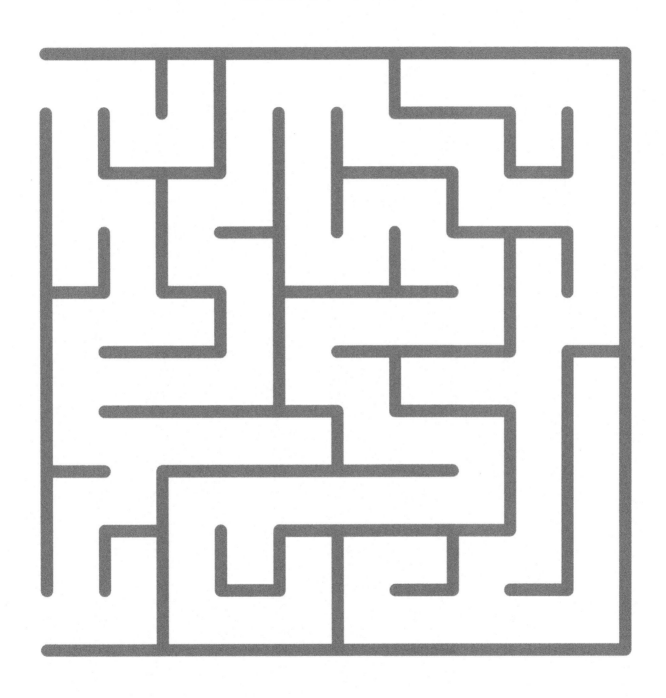

Brain Power!

Brain Power!

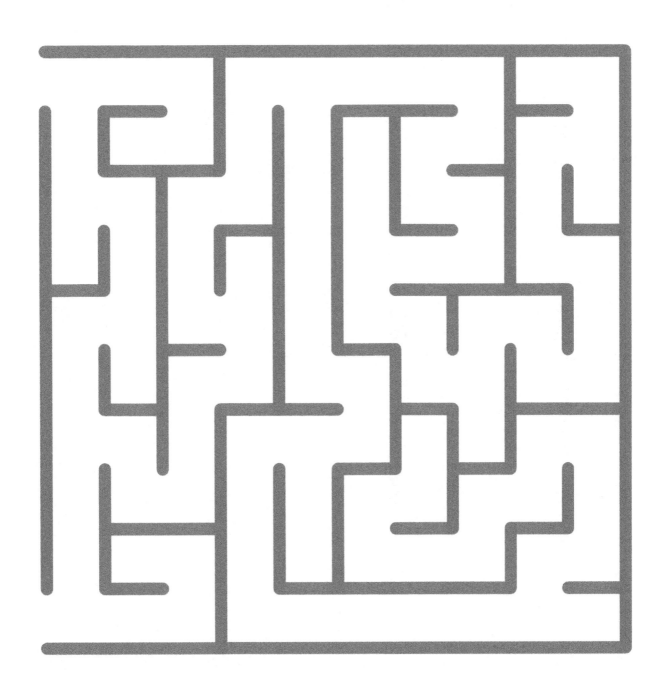

Brain Power!

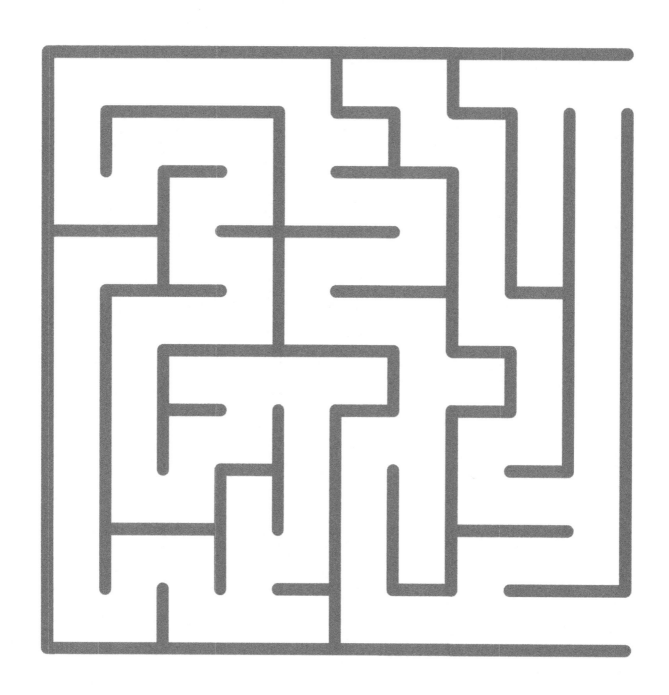

Brain Power!

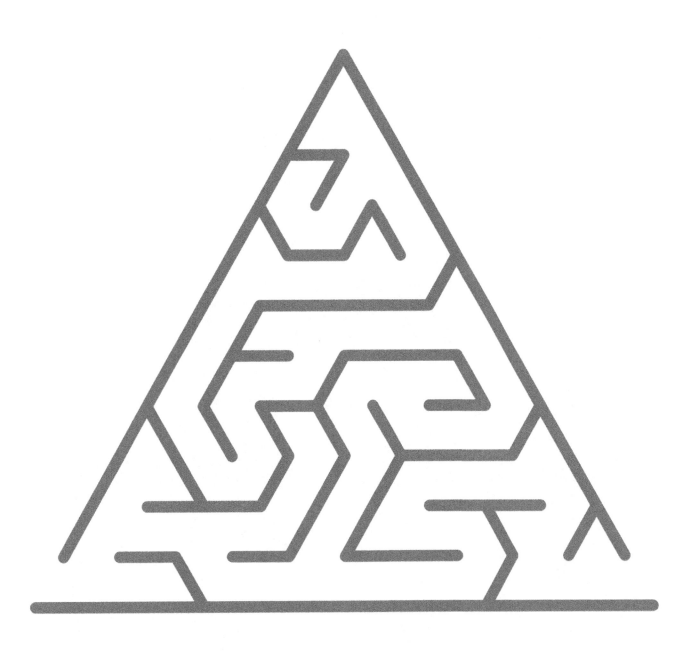

Brain Power!

Brain Power!

Brain Power!

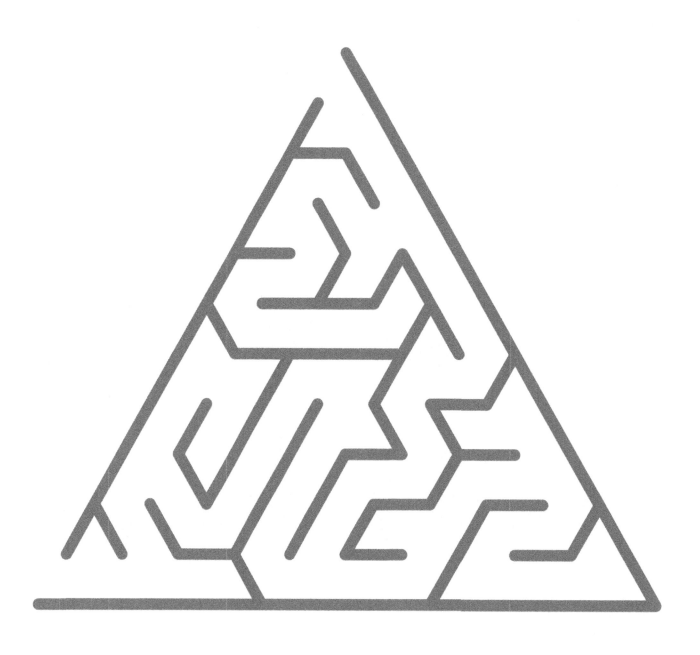

Brain Power!

Brain Power!

Brain Power!

Brain Power!

Brain Power!

Brain Power!

Brain Power!

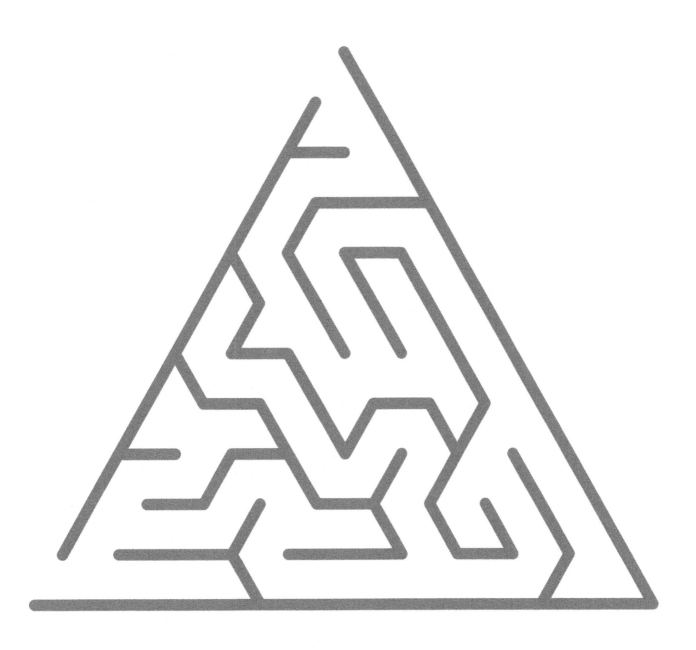

Brain Power!

Brain Power!

Brain Power!

Brain Power!

Brain Power!

Brain Power!

Brain Power!

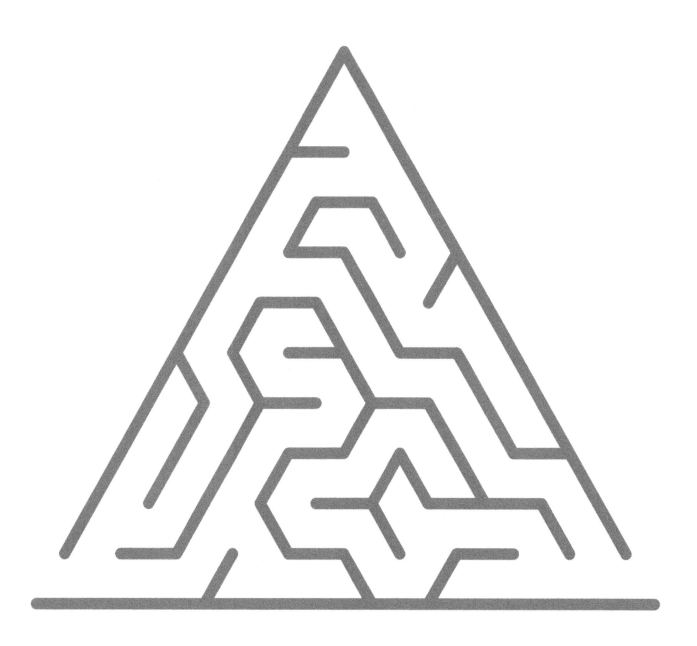

Brain Power!

Brain Power!

Brain Power!

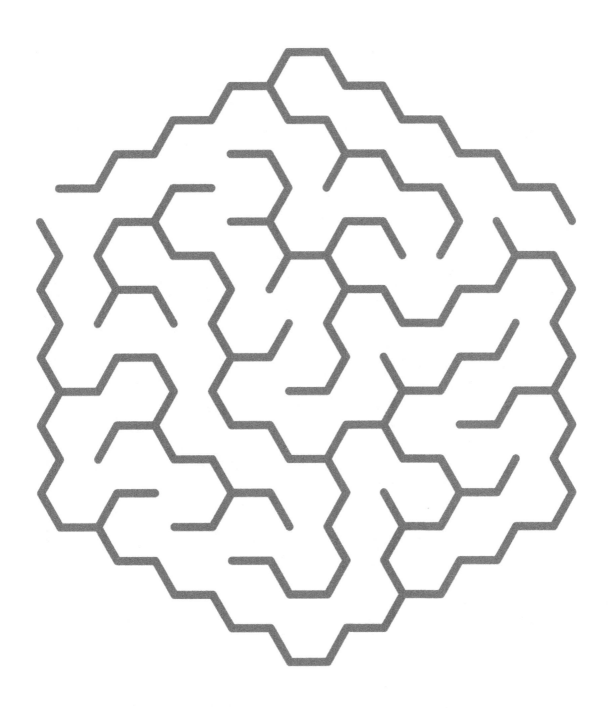

Brain Power!

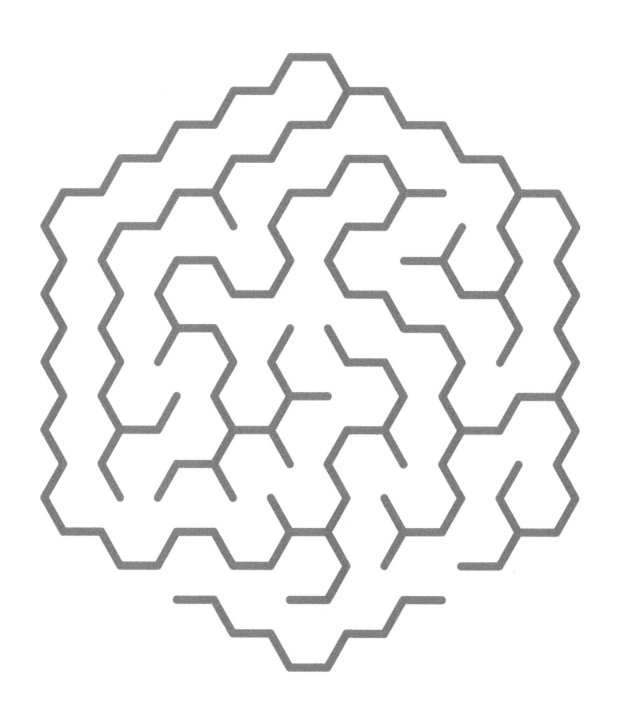

Brain Power!

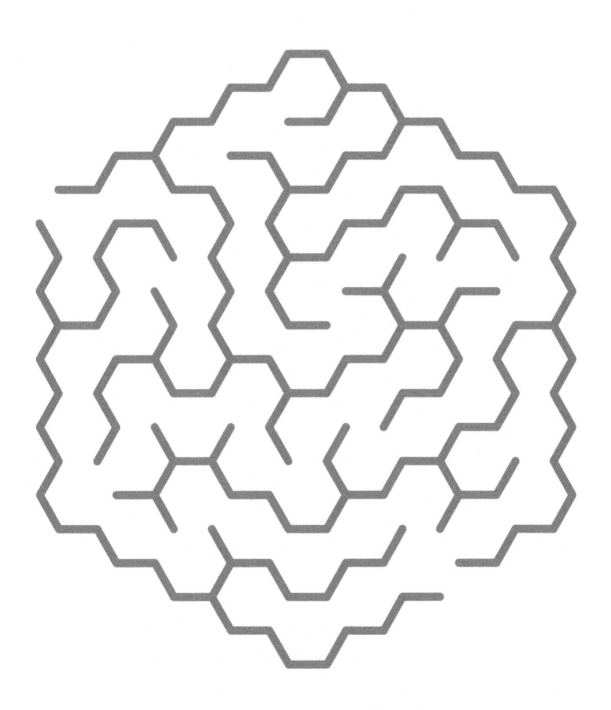

Brain Power!

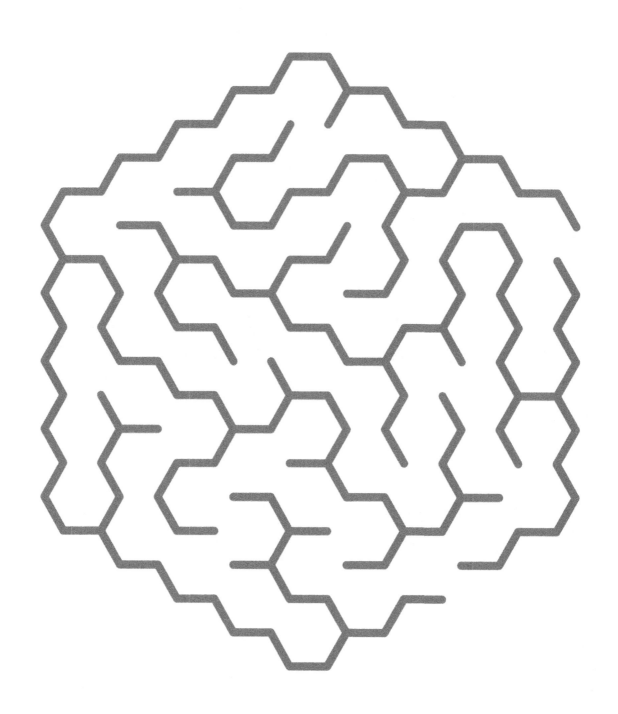

Brain Power!

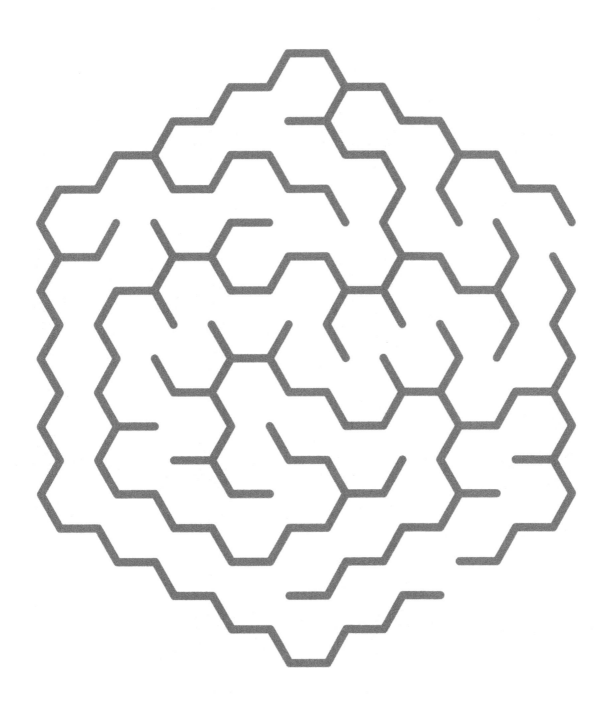

Brain Power!

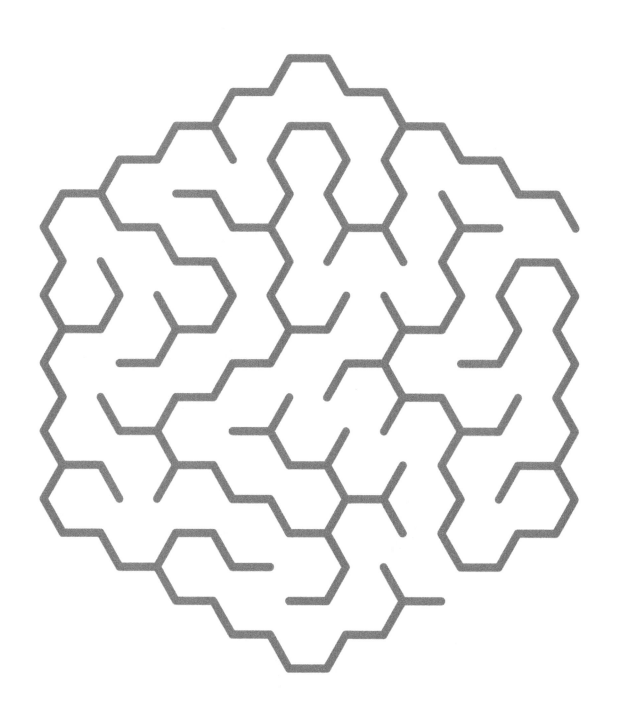

Brain Power!

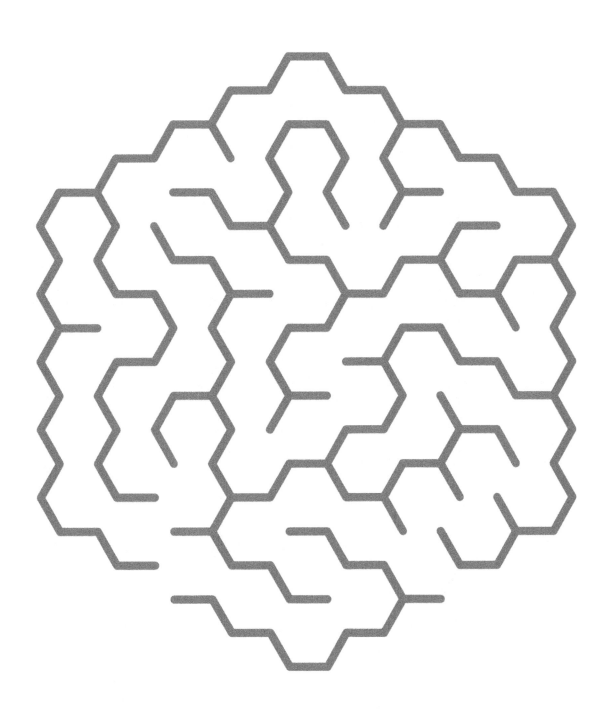

Brain Power!

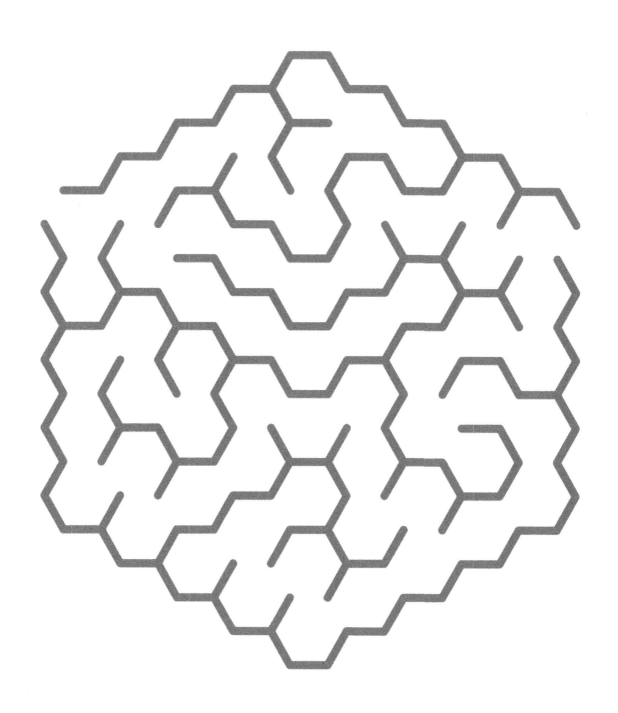

Brain Power!

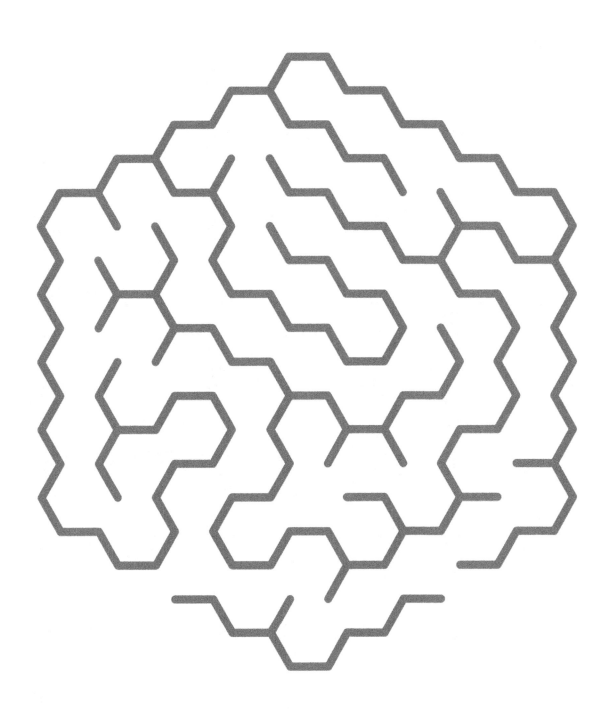

Brain Power!

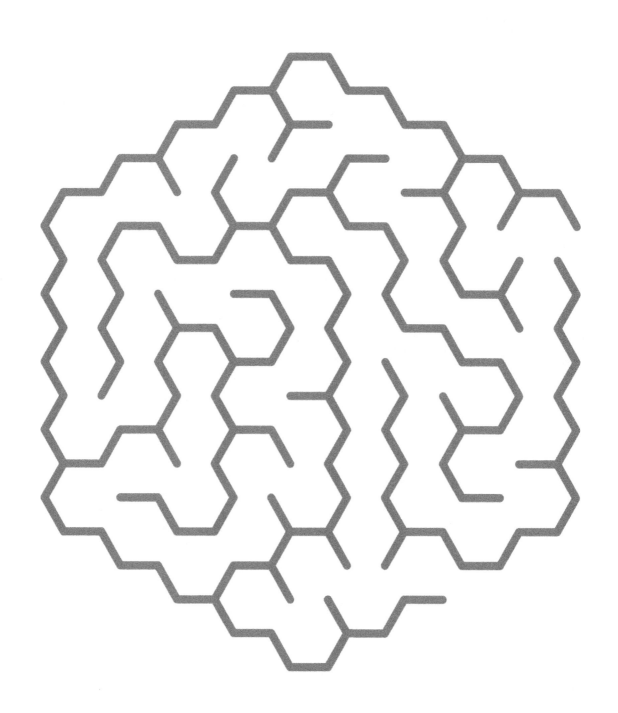

Brain Power!

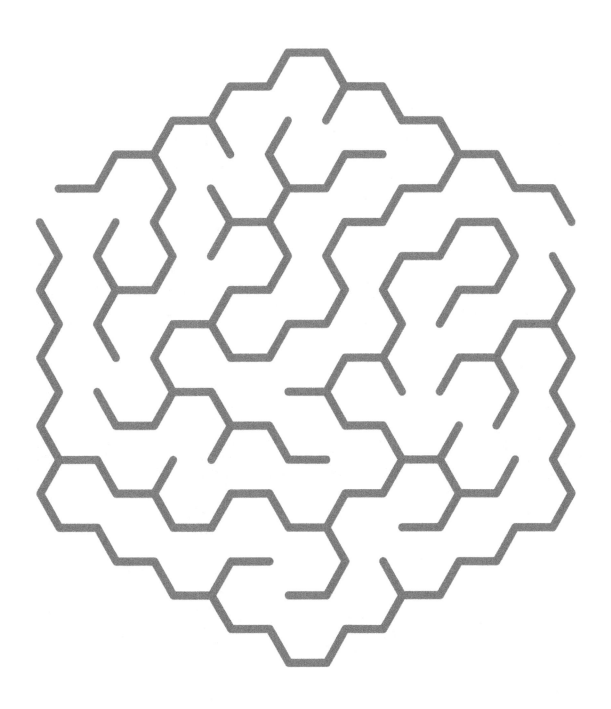

Brain Power!

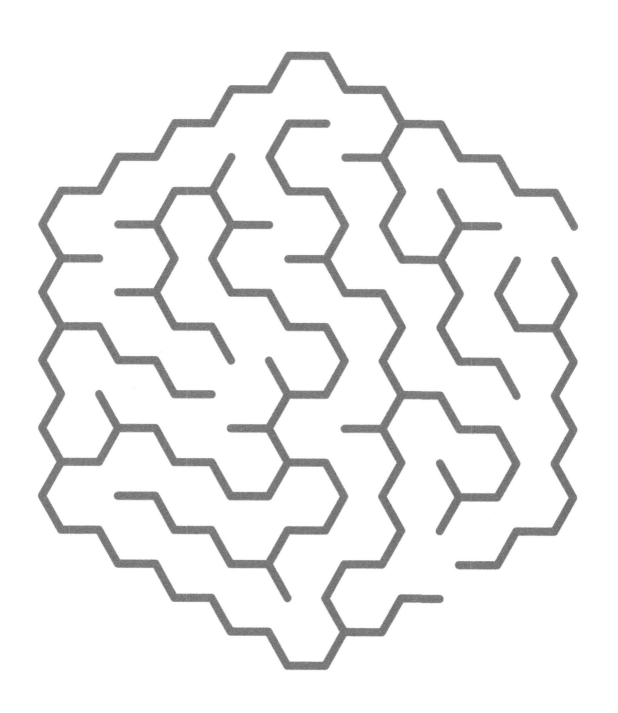

Brain Power!

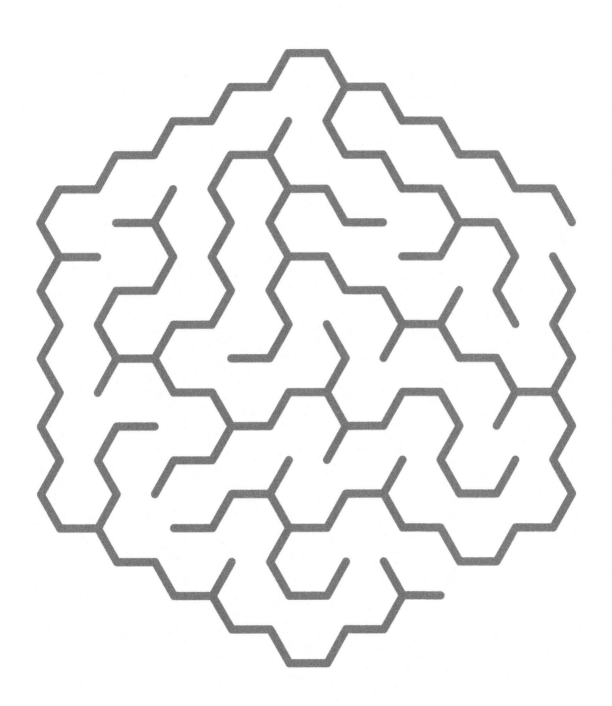

Brain Power!

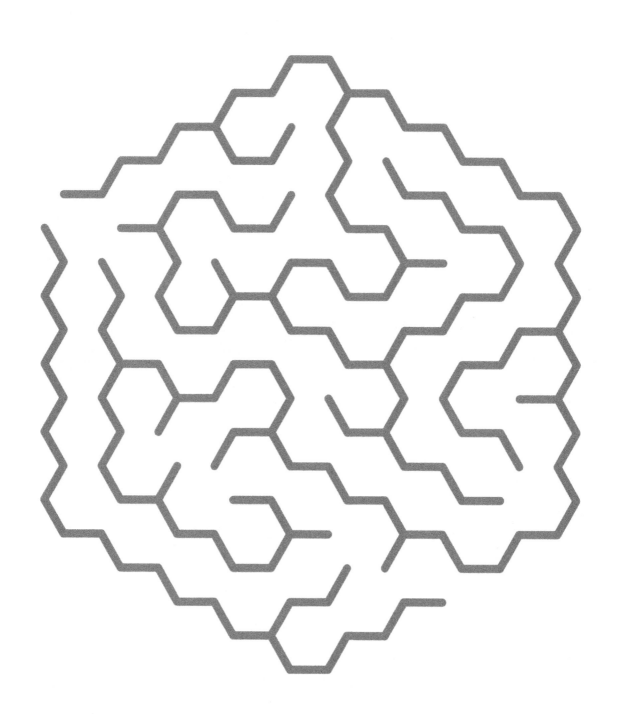

Brain Power!

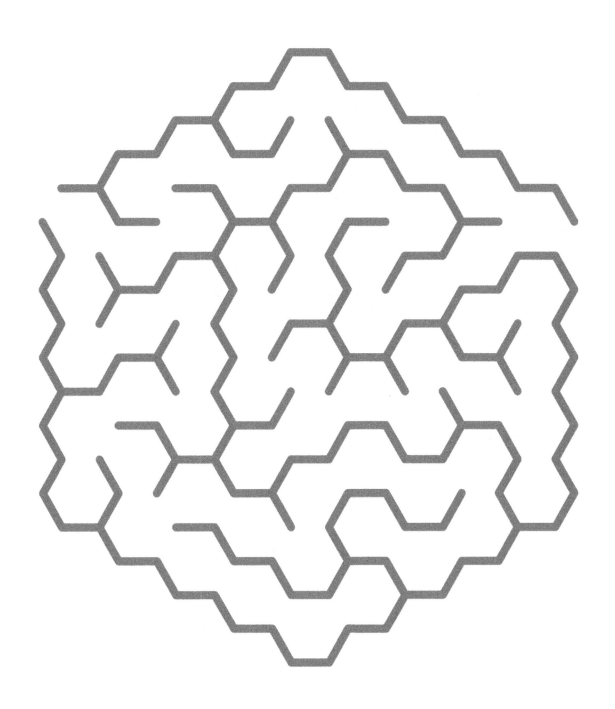

Brain Power!

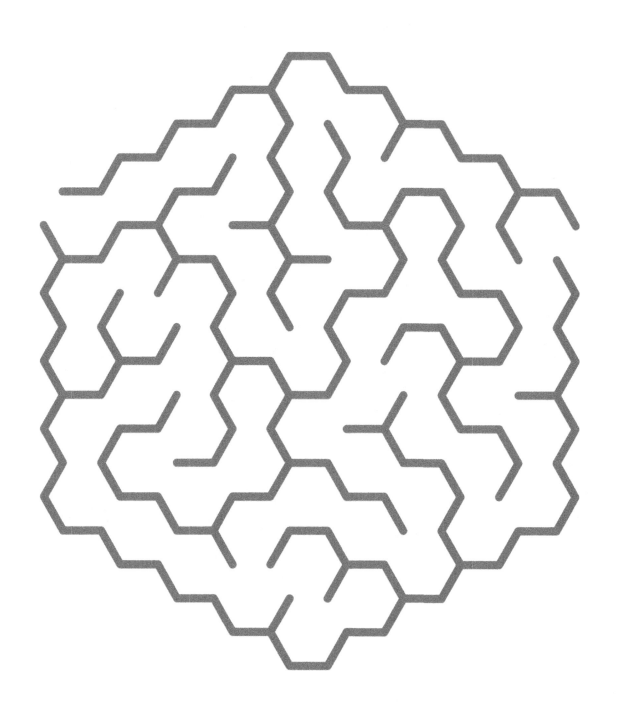

Brain Power!

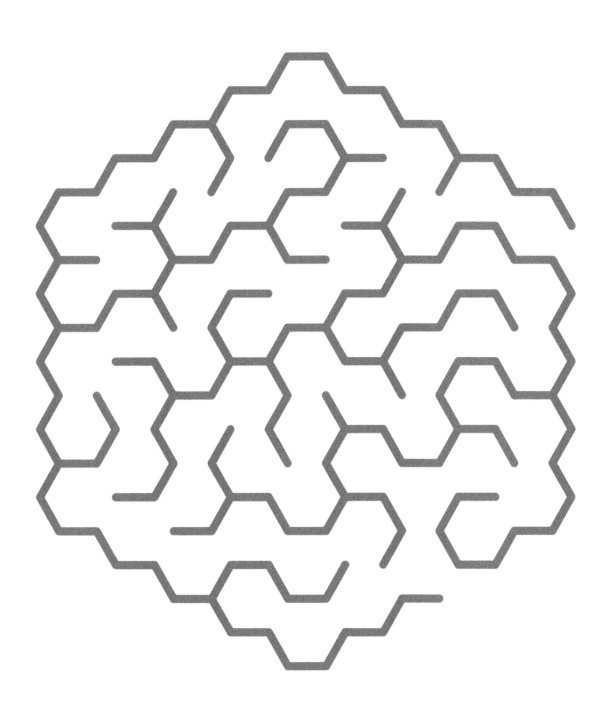

Brain Power!

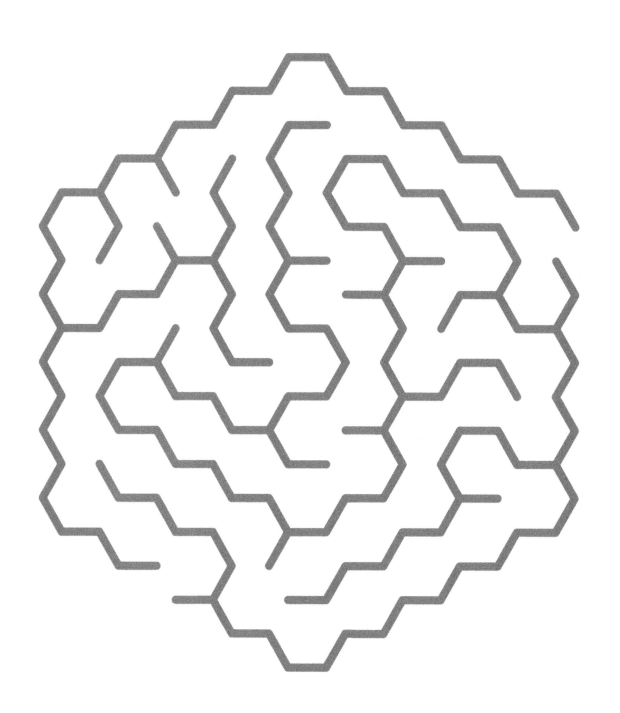

Brain Power!

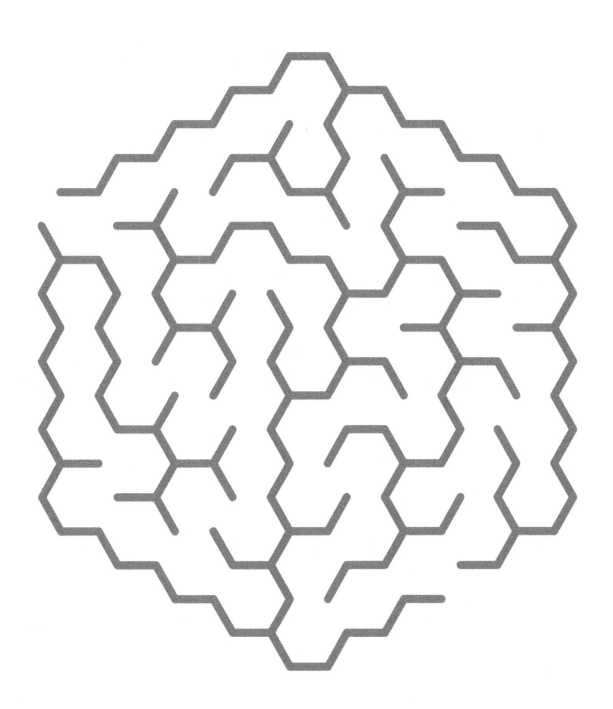

Brain Power!

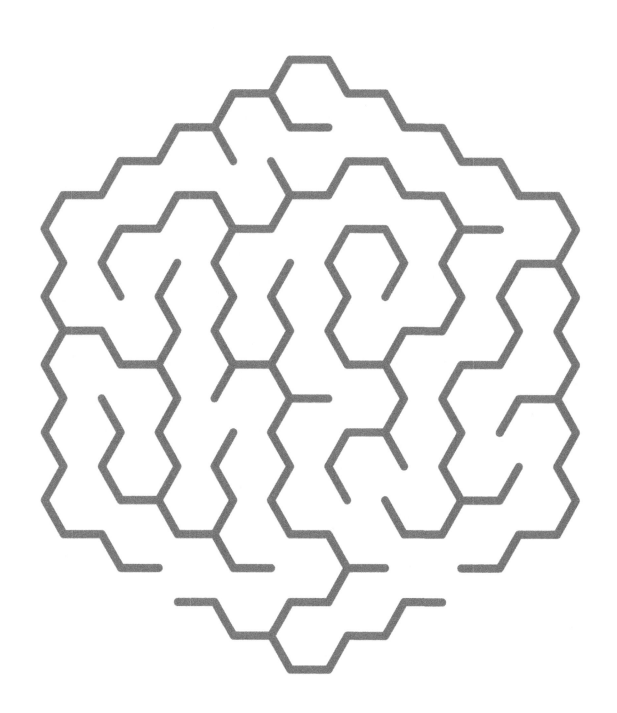

Brain Power!

Brain Power!

Brain Power!

Brain Power!

Brain Power!

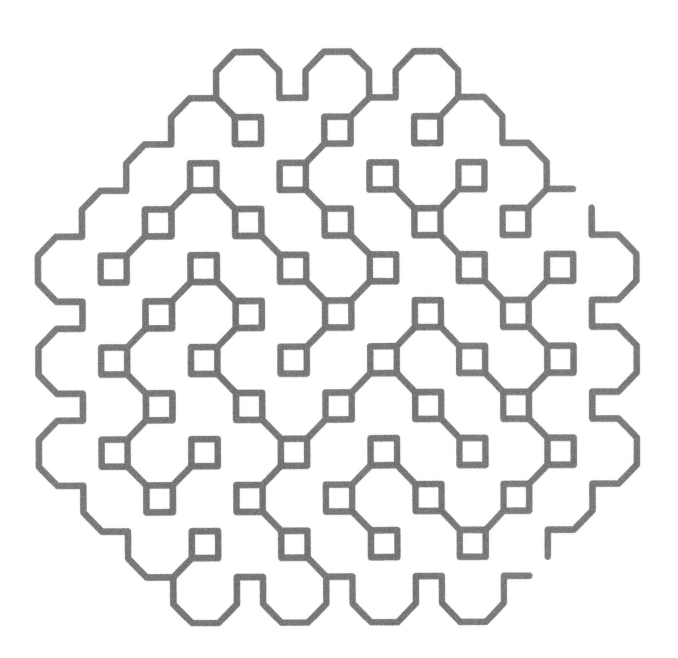

Brain Power!

Brain Power!

Brain Power!

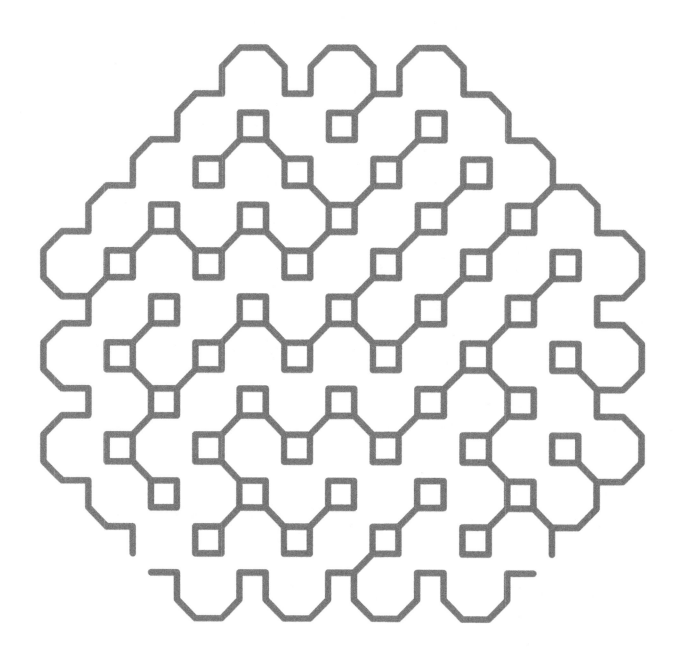

Brain Power!

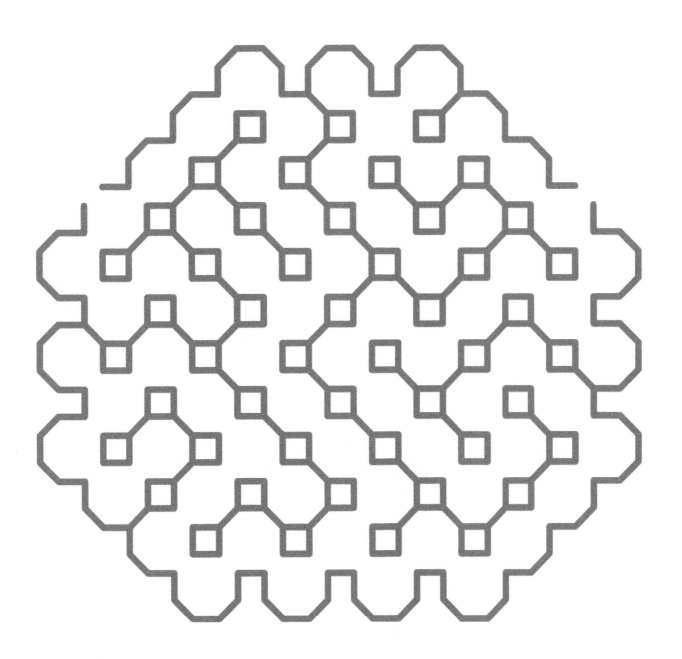

Brain Power!

Brain Power!

Brain Power!

Brain Power!

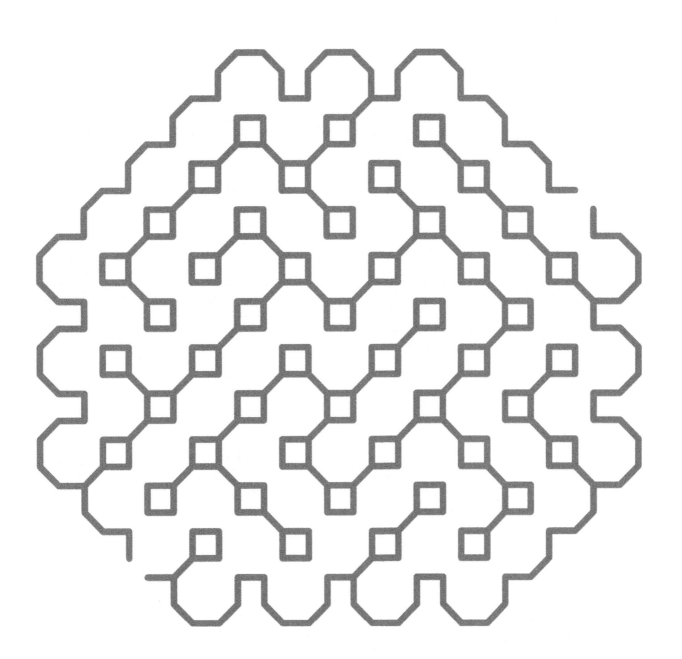

Brain Power!

Brain Power!

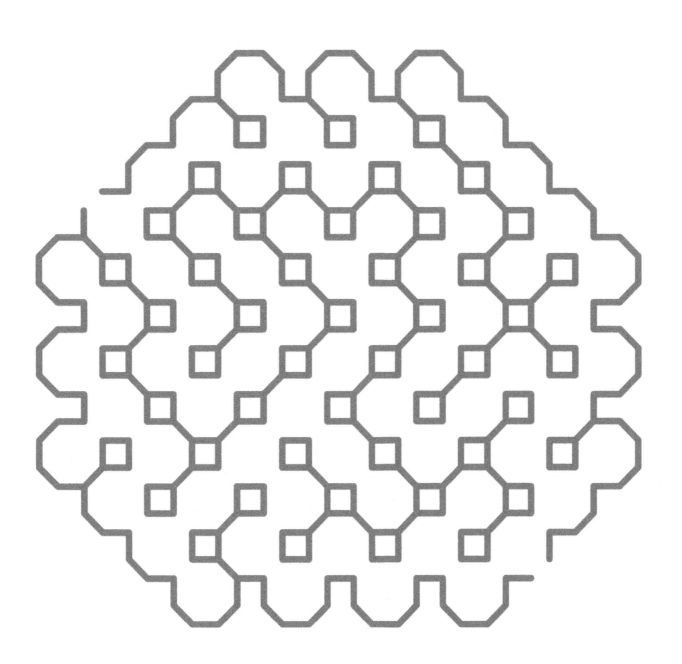

Brain Power!

Brain Power!

Brain Power!

Brain Power!

Brain Power!

Brain Power!

Brain Power!

Brain Power!

Brain Power!

Brain Power!

Brain Power!

Brain Power!

Brain Power!

Brain Power!

Brain Power!

Brain Power!

Brain Power!

Brain Power!

Brain Power!

Brain Power!

Brain Power!

Brain Power!

Brain Power!

Brain Power!

Brain Power!

Brain Power!

Brain Power!

Brain Power!

Brain Power!

Brain Power!

Brain Power!

Brain Power!

Brain Power!

Brain Power!

Brain Power!

Brain Power!

Brain Power!

Brain Power!

Brain Power!

Brain Power!

Brain Power!

Brain Power!

Brain Power!

Brain Power!

Brain Power!

Brain Power!

Brain Power!

Brain Power!

Brain Power!

Brain Power!

Brain Power!

Brain Power!

Brain Power!

Brain Power!

Brain Power!

Brain Power!

Brain Power!

Brain Power!

Brain Power!

Brain Power!

Brain Power!

Brain Power!

Brain Power!

Brain Power!

Brain Power!

Brain Power!

Brain Power!

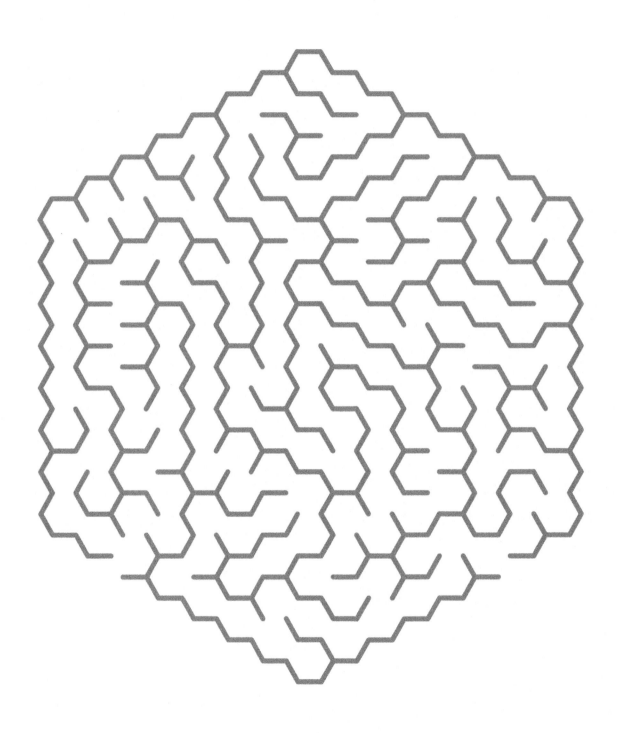

Brain Power!

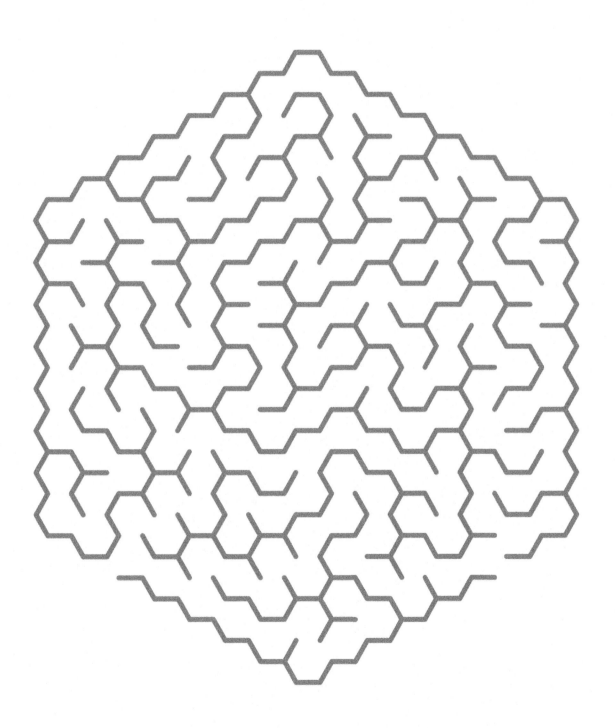

Brain Power!

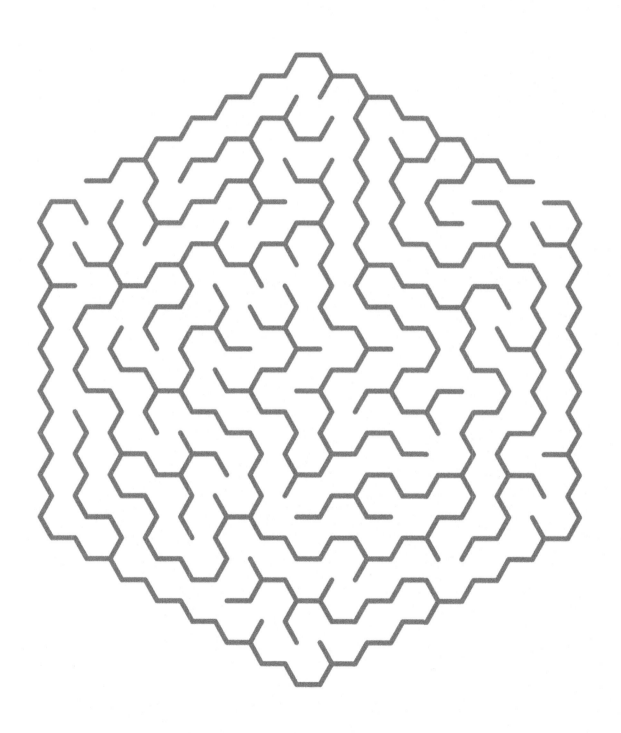

Brain Power!

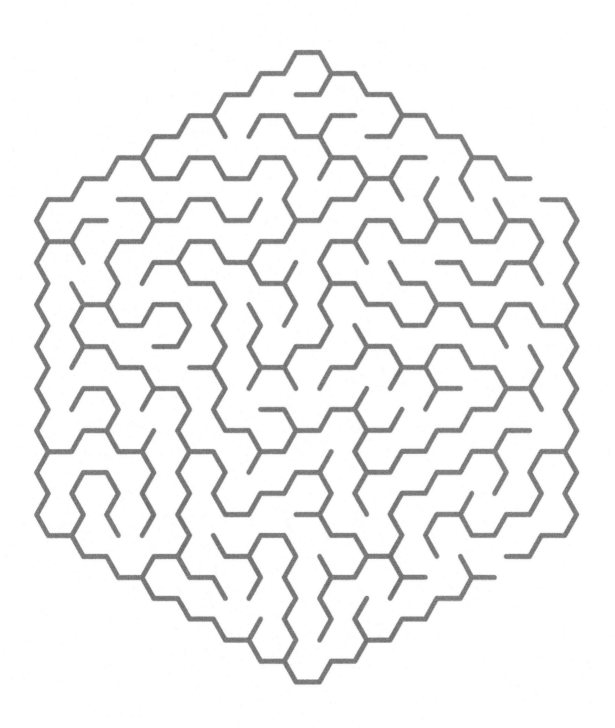

Brain Power!

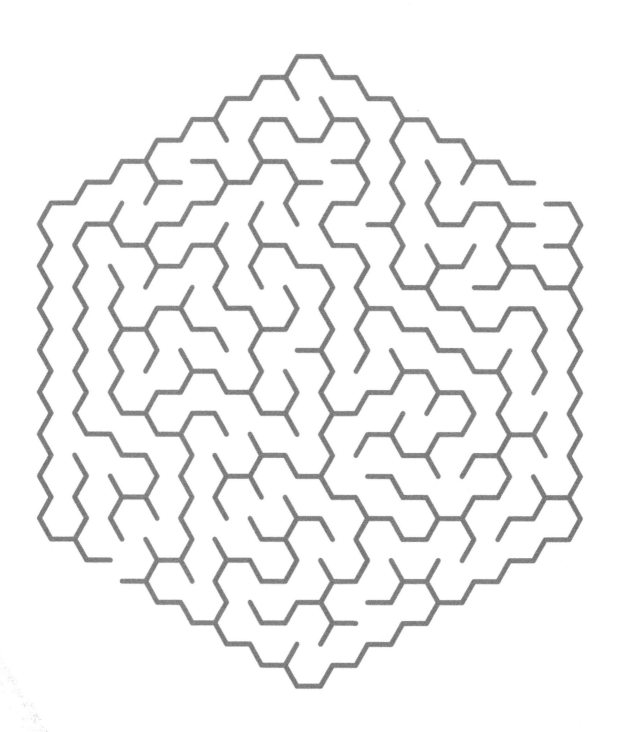

Brain Power!

Brain Power!

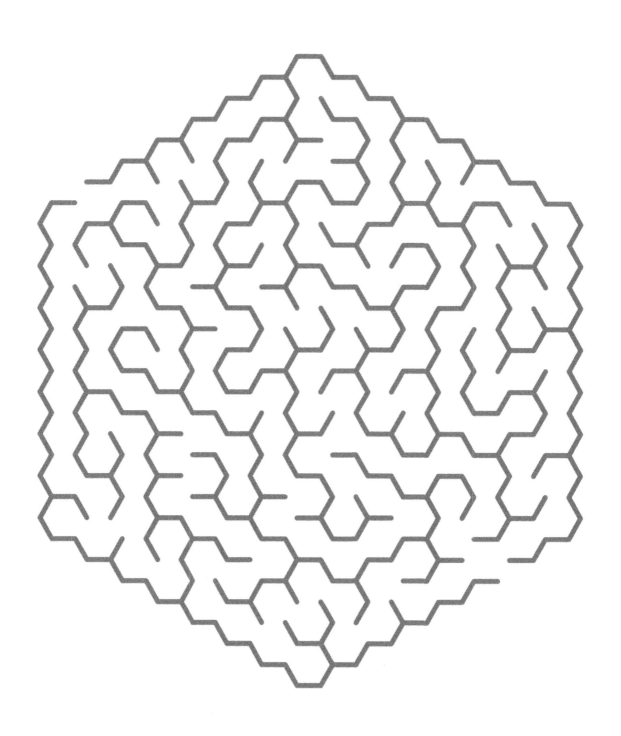

Brain Power!

Brain Power!

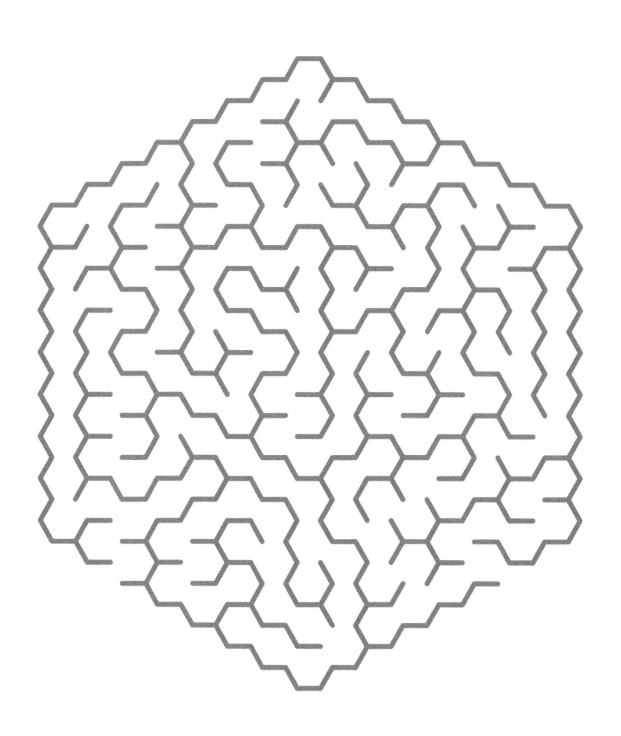

Brain Power!

Brain Power!

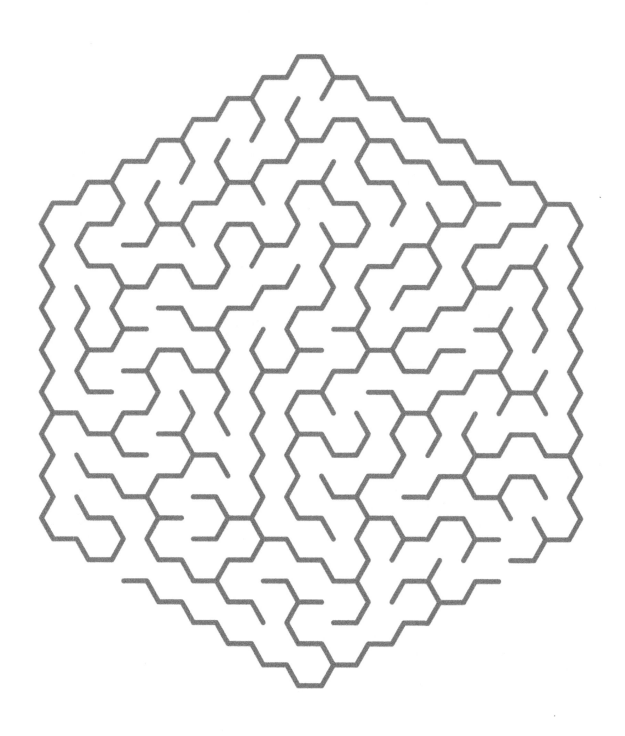

Brain Power!

Brain Power!

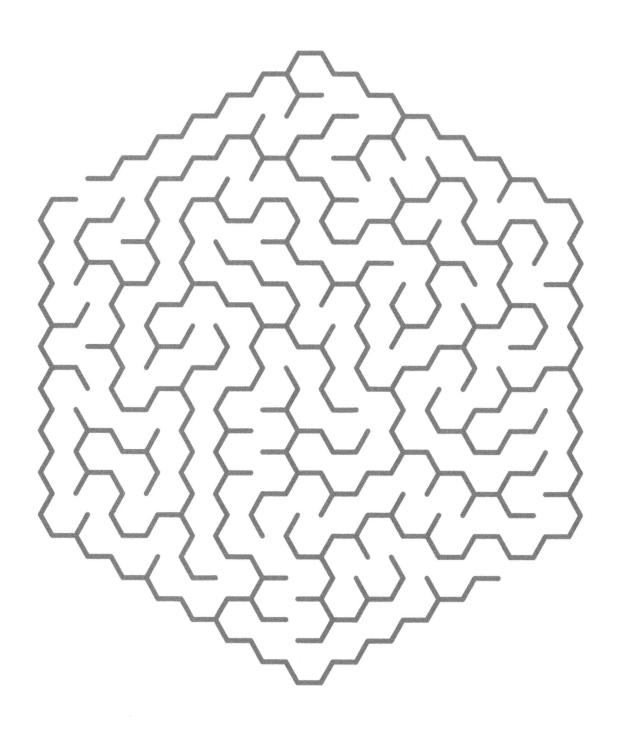

Brain Power!

Brain Power!

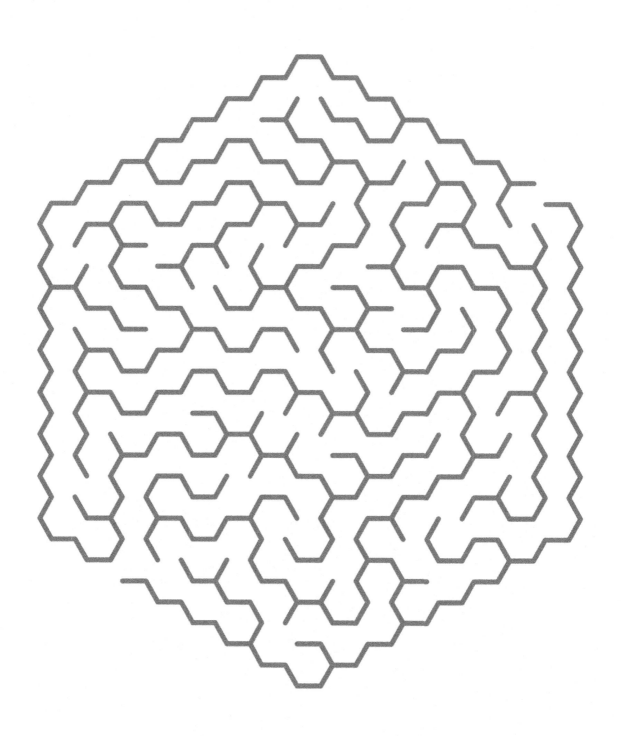

Brain Power!

Brain Power!

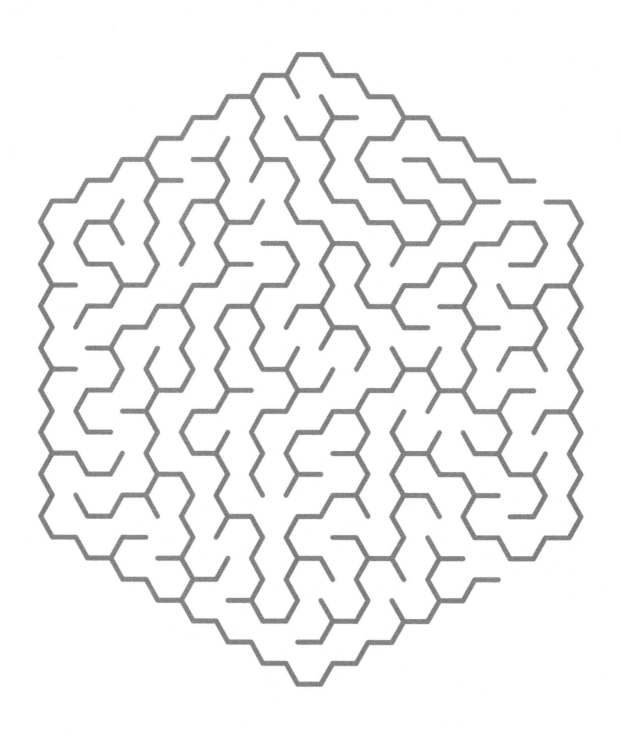

Brain Power!

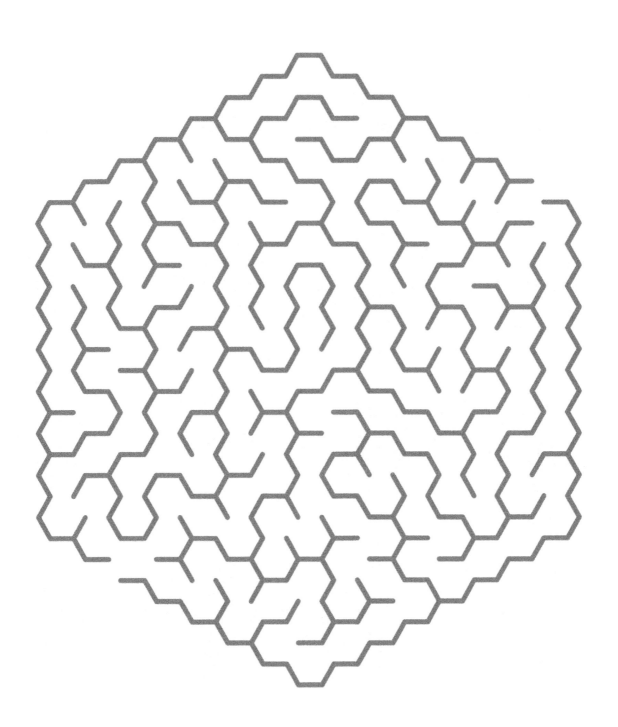

Brain Power!

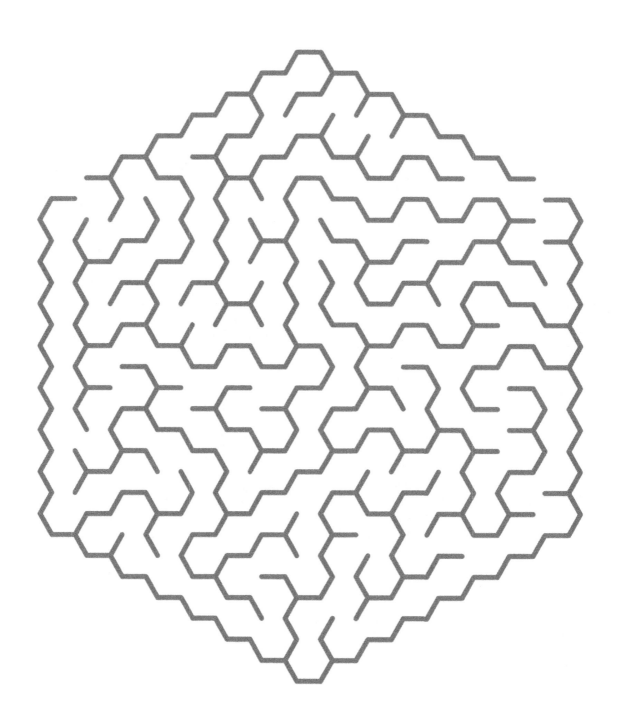

Brain Power!

Brain Power!

Brain Power!

Brain Power!

Brain Power!

Brain Power!

Brain Power!

Brain Power!

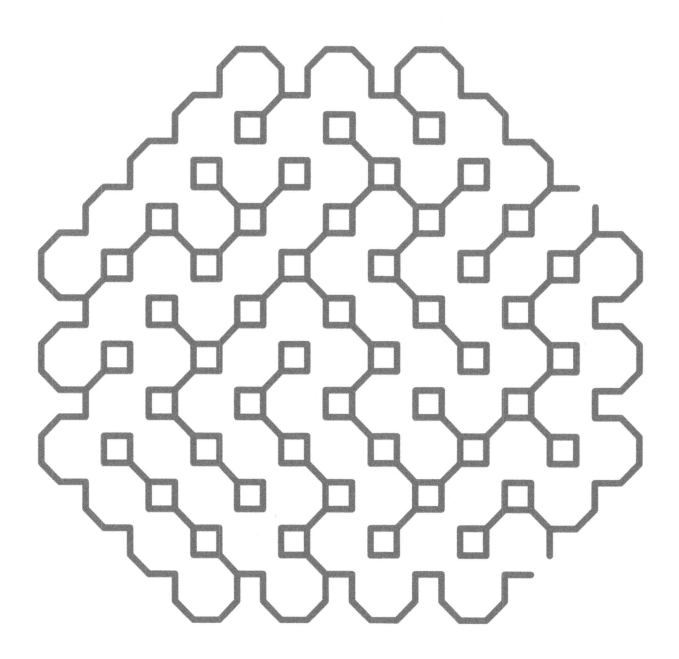

Brain Power!

Brain Power!

Brain Power!

Brain Power!

Brain Power!

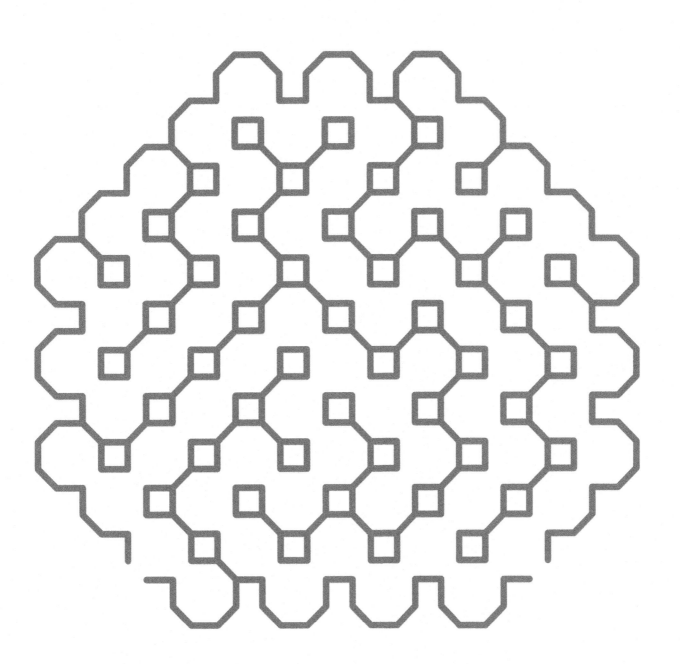

Brain Power!

Brain Power!

Brain Power!

Brain Power!

Brain Power!

Brain Power!

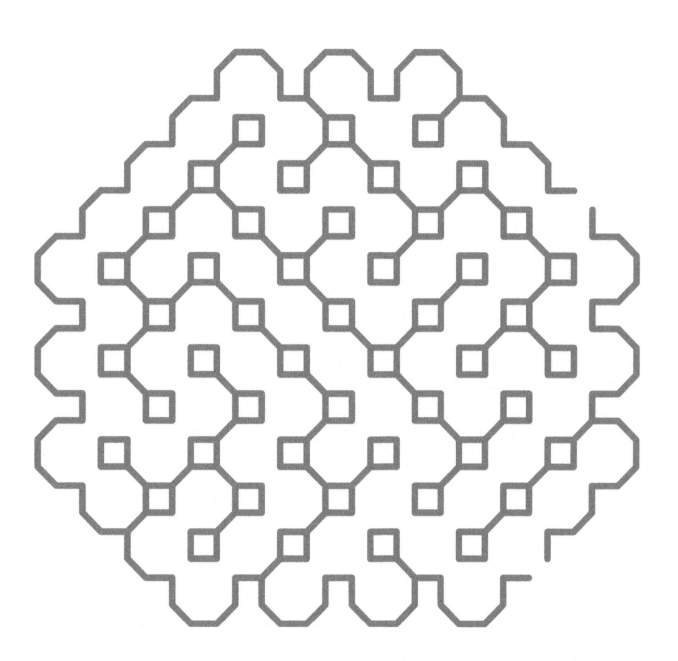

Brain Power!

Brain Power!

Brain Power!

Brain Power!

Brain Power!

Brain Power!

Brain Power!

Brain Power!

Brain Power!

Brain Power!

Brain Power!

Brain Power!

Brain Power!

Brain Power!

Brain Power!

Brain Power!

Brain Power!

Brain Power!

Brain Power!

Brain Power!

Brain Power!

Page1-1

Page2-1

Page3-1

Page4-1

Page5-1

Page6-1

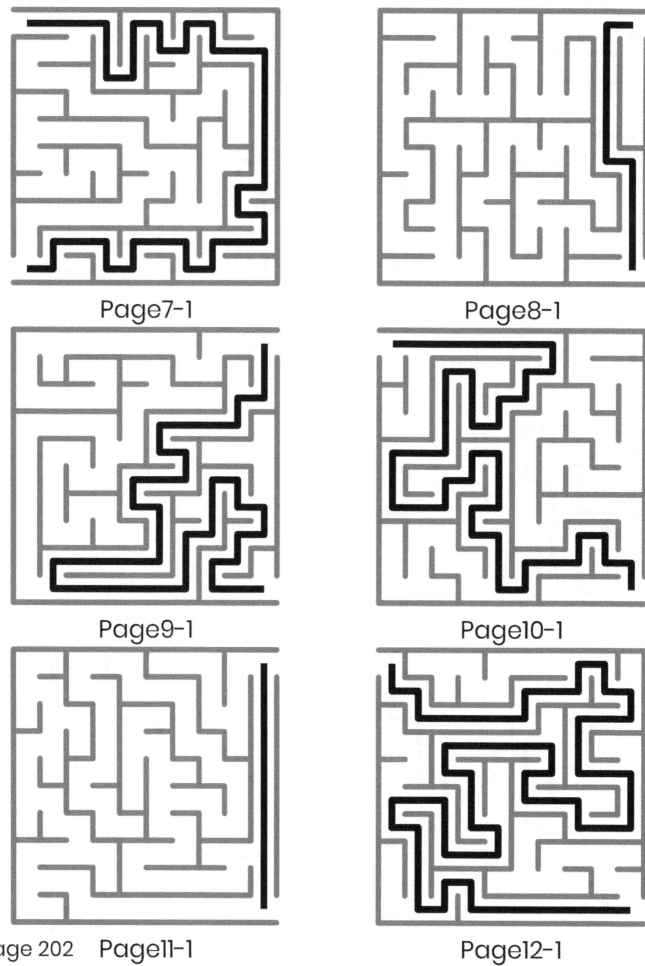

Page7-1

Page8-1

Page9-1

Page10-1

Page11-1

Page12-1

Page13-1

Page14-1

Page15-1

Page16-1

Page17-1

Page18-1 Page 203

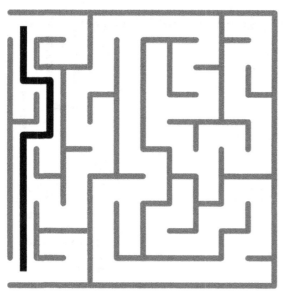

Page19-1

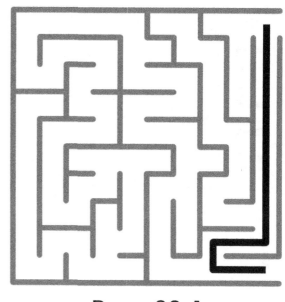

Page20-1

Page21-1

Page22-1

Page23-1

Page24-1

Page25-1

Page26-1

Page27-1

Page28-1

Page29-1

Page30-1

Page31-1

Page32-1

Page33-1

Page34-1

Page35-1

Page36-1

Page37-1

Page38-1

Page39-1

Page40-1

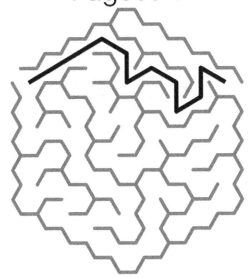

Page41-1

Page42-1

Page43-1

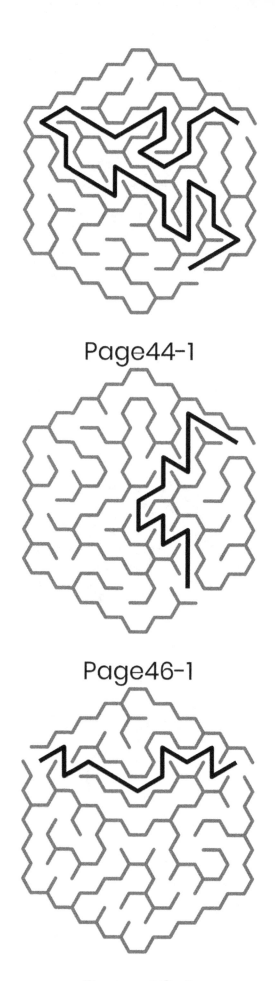

Page44-1

Page45-1

Page46-1

Page 208   Page47-1

Page48-1

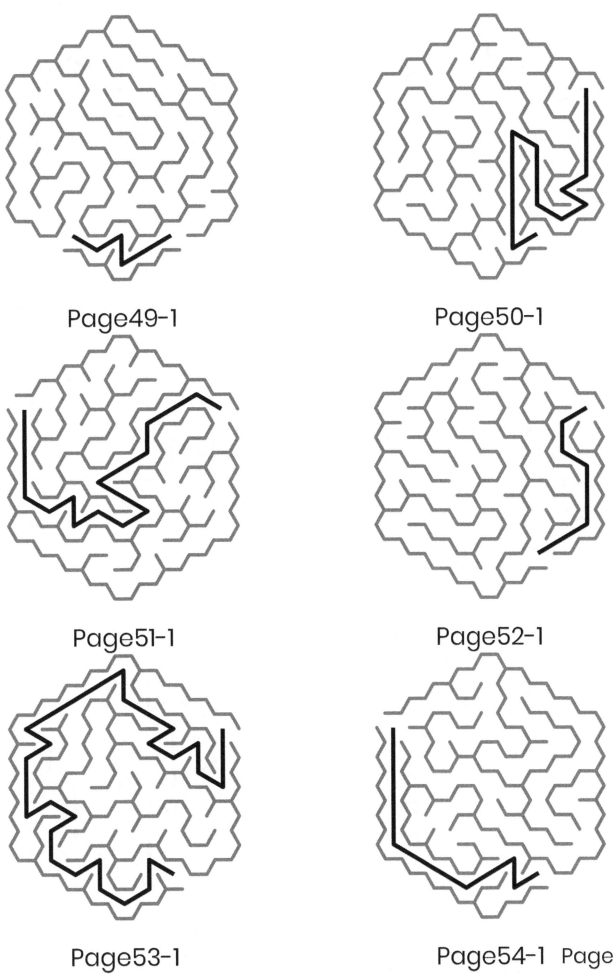

Page49-1

Page50-1

Page51-1

Page52-1

Page53-1

Page54-1

Page55-1

Page56-1

Page57-1

Page58-1

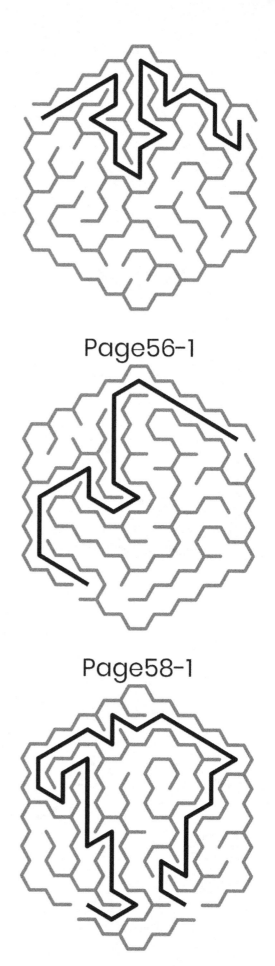

Page59-1

Page60-1

Page61-1

Page62-1

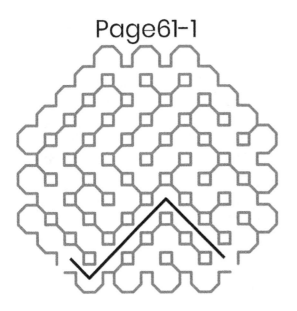

Page63-1

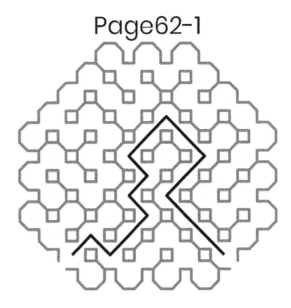

Page64-1

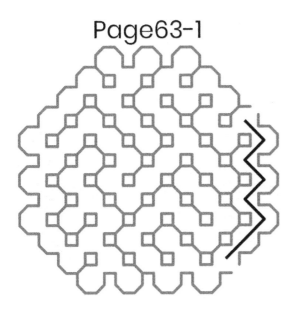

Page65-1

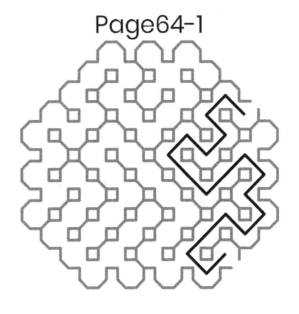

Page66-1

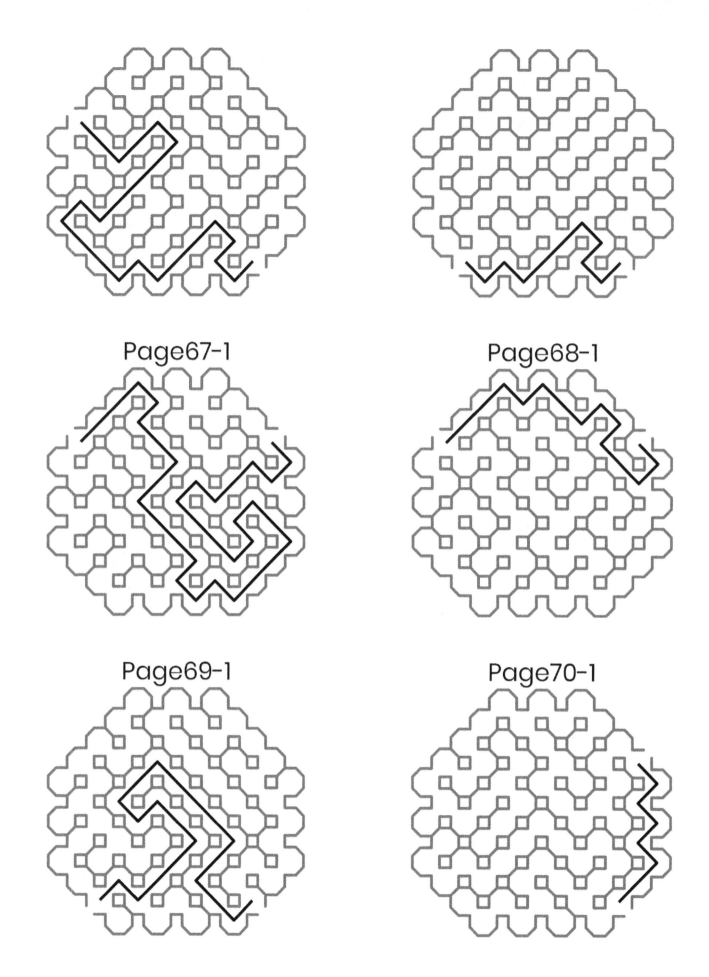

Page67-1

Page68-1

Page69-1

Page70-1

Page71-1

Page72-1

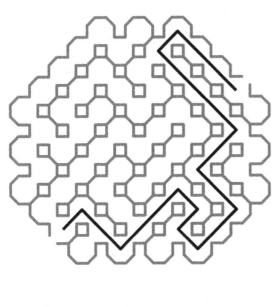

Page73-1

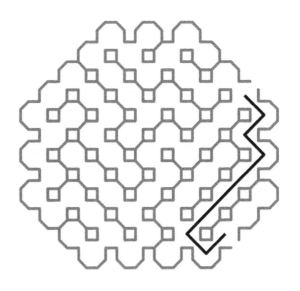

Page74-1

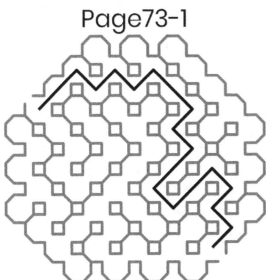

Page75-1

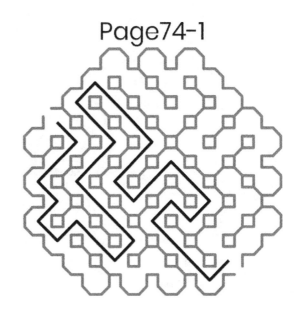

Page76-1

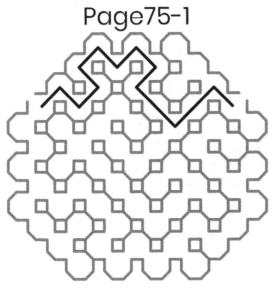

Page77-1

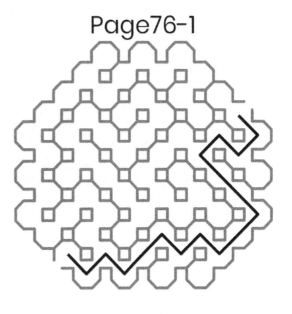

Page78-1

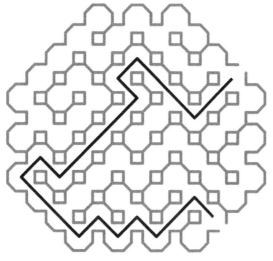

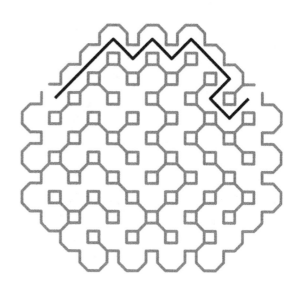

Page79-1

Page80-1

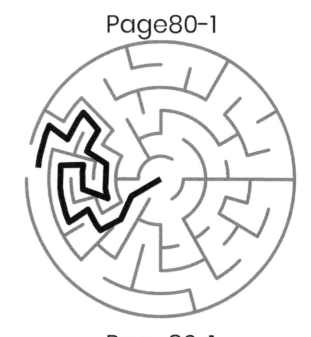

Page81-1

Page82-1

Page83-1

Page84-1

Page85-1

Page86-1

Page87-1

Page88-1

Page89-1

Page90-1   Page 215

Page91-1

Page92-1

Page93-1

Page94-1

Page95-1

Page96-1

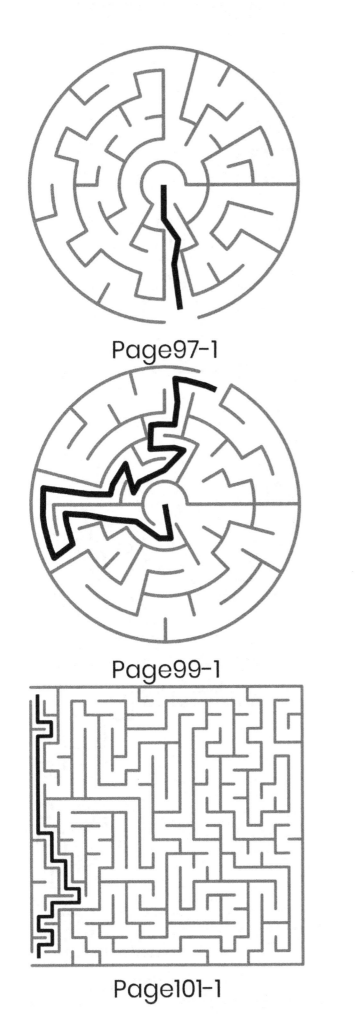

Page97-1

Page98-1

Page99-1

Page100-1

Page101-1

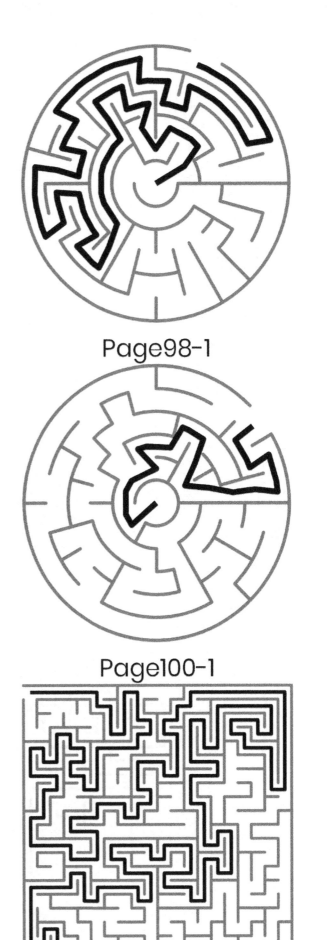

Page102-1

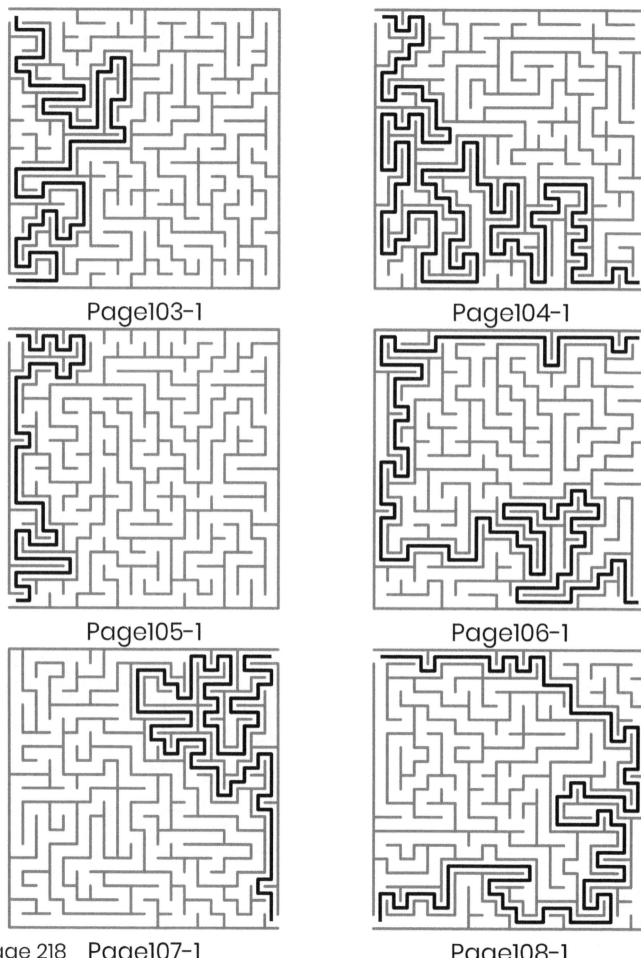

Page103-1

Page104-1

Page105-1

Page106-1

Page107-1

Page108-1

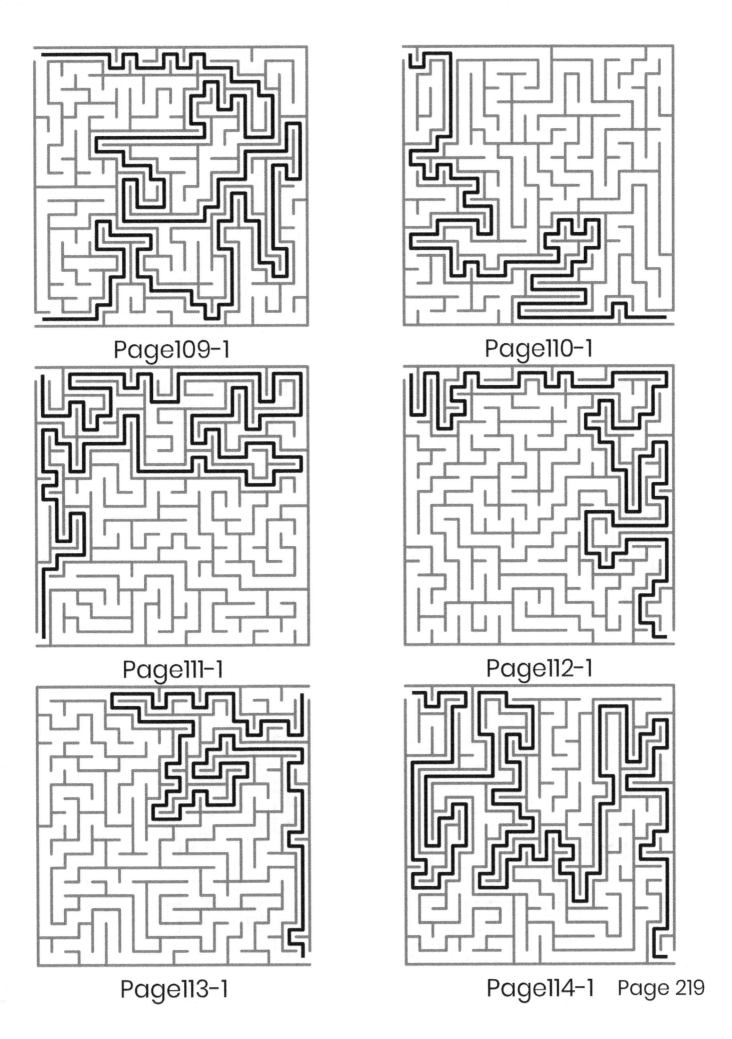

Page109-1

Page110-1

Page111-1

Page112-1

Page113-1

Page114-1

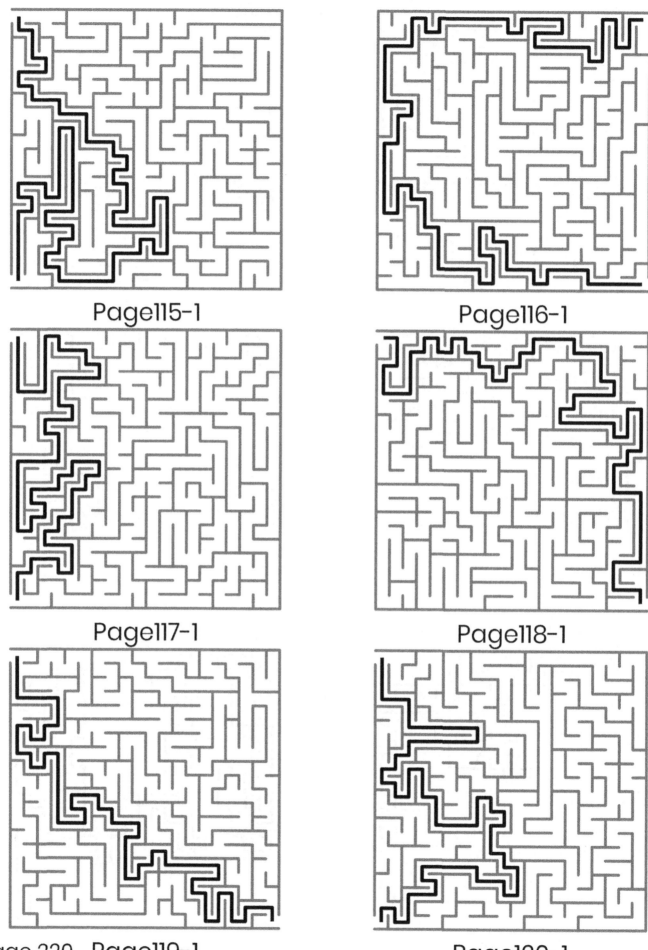

Page115-1

Page116-1

Page117-1

Page118-1

Page119-1

Page120-1

Page121-1

Page122-1

Page123-1

Page124-1

Page125-1

Page126-1 Page 221

Page127-1

Page128-1

Page129-1

Page130-1

Page131-1

Page132-1

Page133-1

Page134-1

Page135-1

Page136-1

Page137-1

Page138-1

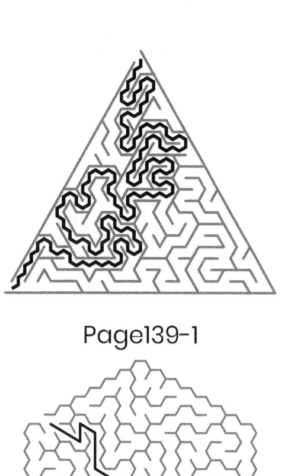

Page139-1

Page140-1

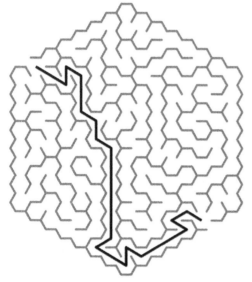

Page141-1

Page142-1

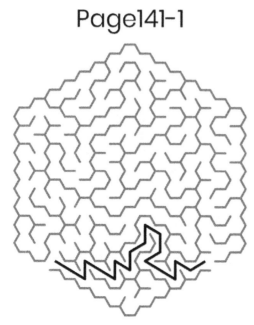

Page143-1

Page144-1

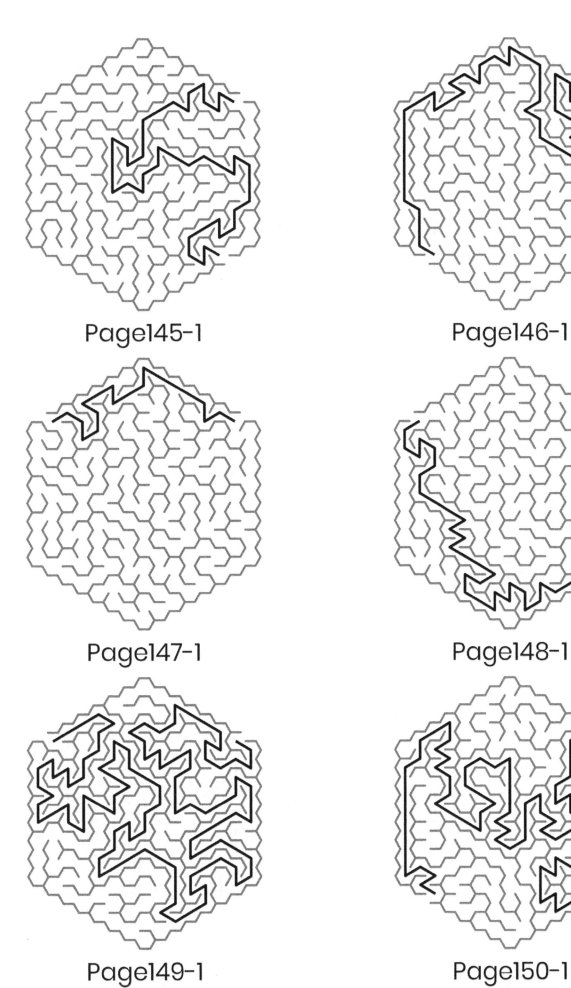

Page145-1

Page146-1

Page147-1

Page148-1

Page149-1

Page150-1

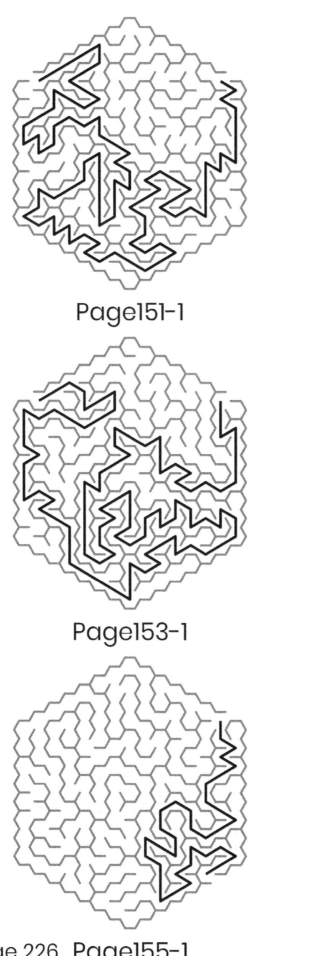

Page151-1

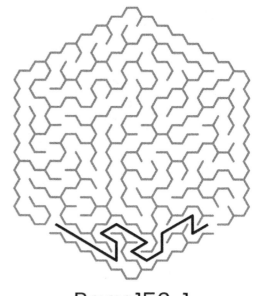

Page152-1

Page153-1

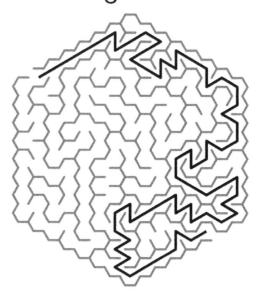

Page154-1

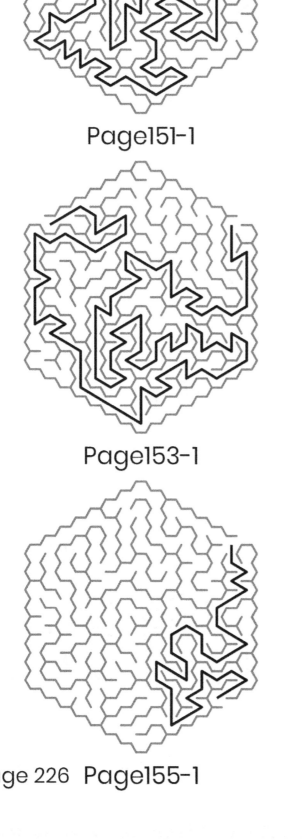

Page155-1

Page156-1

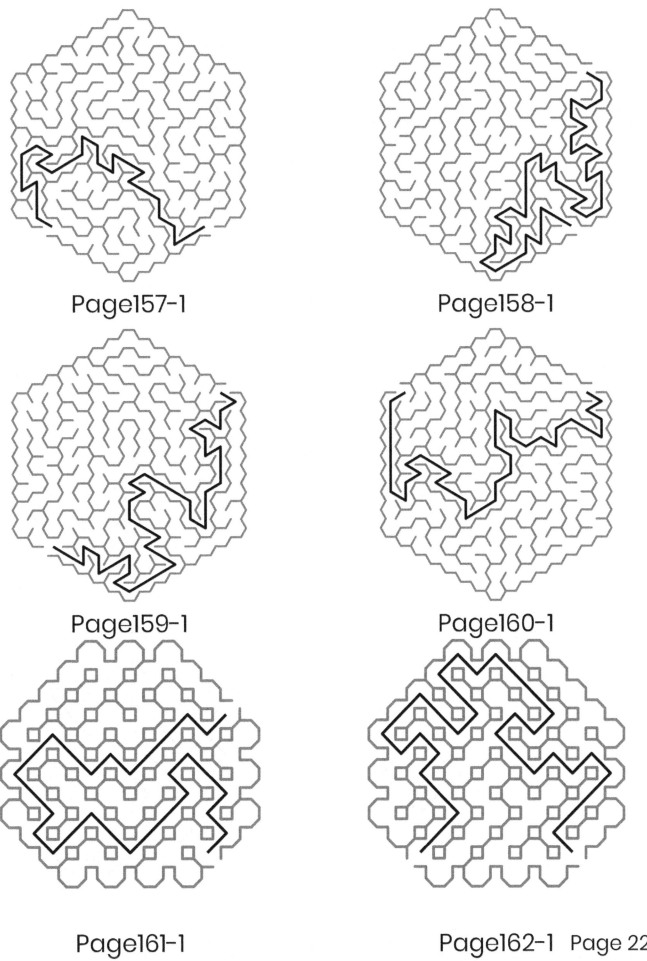

Page157-1

Page158-1

Page159-1

Page160-1

Page161-1

Page162-1 Page 227

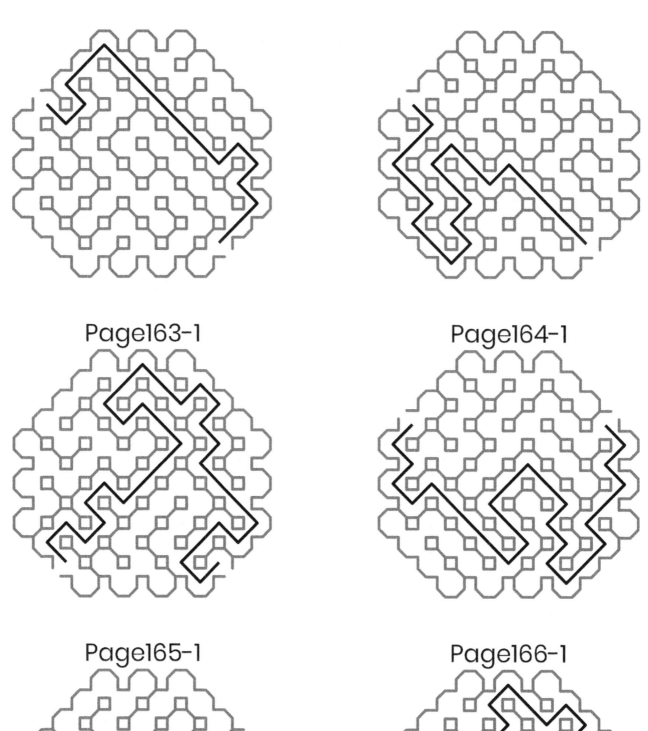

Page163-1

Page164-1

Page165-1

Page166-1

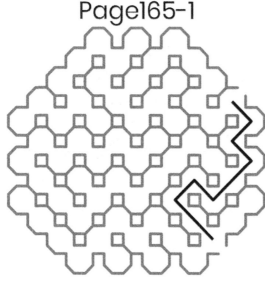

Page167-1

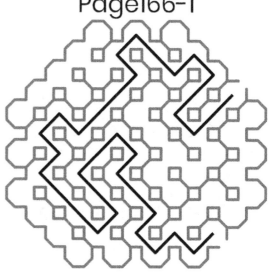

Page168-1

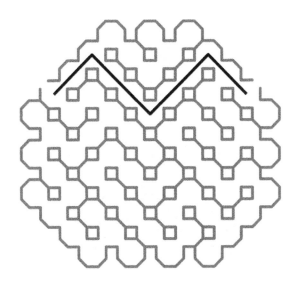

Page169-1

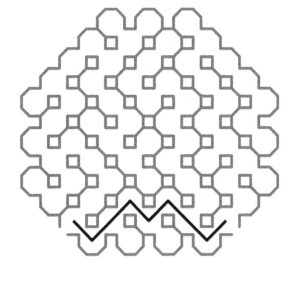

Page170-1

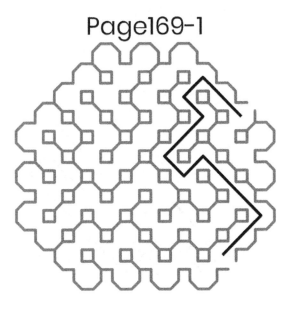

Page171-1

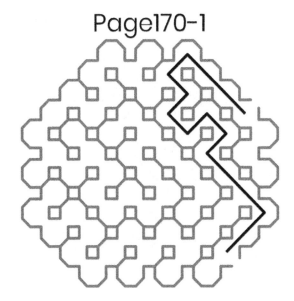

Page172-1

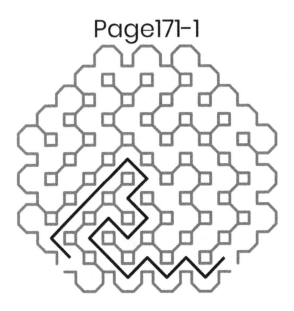

Page173-1

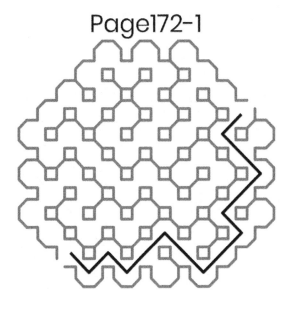

Page174-1

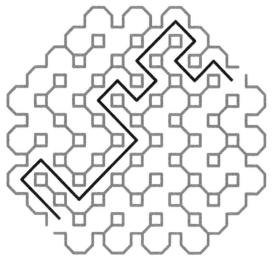

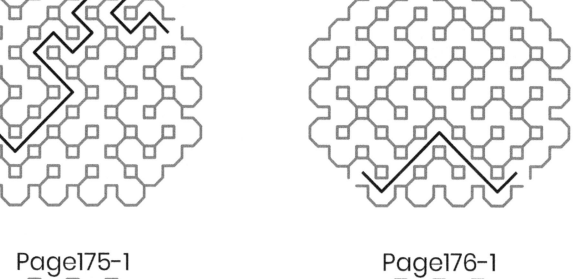

Page175-1

Page176-1

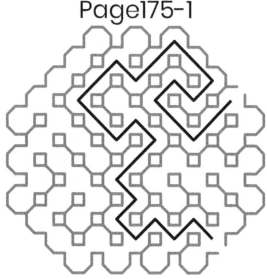

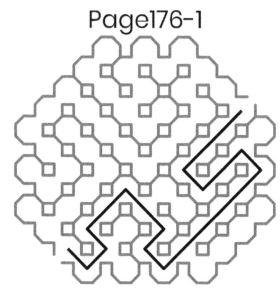

Page177-1

Page178-1

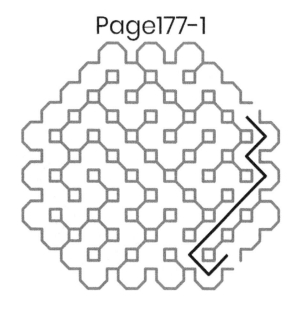

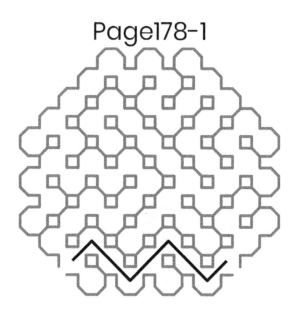

Page179-1

Page180-1

Page181-1

Page182-1

Page183-1

Page184-1

Page185-1

Page186-1   Page 231

Page187-1

Page188-1

Page189-1

Page190-1

Page 232   Page191-1

Page192-1

Page193-1

Page194-1

Page195-1

Page196-1

Page197-1

Page198-1 Page 233

Page199-1

Page200-1